BASIC WELDING

Hopwood Hall College, Rochdale

BASIC WELDING

Stuart W. Gibson
Sen. M. Weld. I., MAWS, MAWTE, DME
*Lecturer in Charge of Welding,
Hopwood Hall College,
and Postgraduate Researcher in Welding,
Manchester University*

and

Alan R. Smith

*Former Lecturer in Charge of Welding,
Hopwood Hall College*

MACMILLAN

First published 1993 by
THE MACMILLAN PRESS LTD
·Houndmills, Basingstoke, Hampshire RG21 2XS
and London
Companies and representatives
throughout the world

ISBN 0–333–57853–8

A catalogue record for this book is available
from the British Library

Printed in China

10 9 8 7 6 5 4 3 2
01 00 99 98 97 96 95 94 93

To
Sheila

Every effort has been made to ensure that the information contained in this book is accurate at the time of going to press. However, the authors and publisher do not assume responsibility or liability for any applications produced from the information. In welding, the application can vary considerably from job to job and it is the responsibility of the user to carry out work to statutory requirements.

CONTENTS

PREFACE

This book is not intended to provide sophisticated knowledge of fusion techniques and associated background material, but is particularly suitable for preliminary engineering studies.

Students undertaking City and Guilds Welding Courses, the 165 Certificate in Welding Practice, or indeed inquisitive engineers anxious to broaden their scope of activity for professional reasons, will benefit from the contents.

The history of fusion, forging and welding techniques in one form or another, particularly for the manufacture of hunting and defensive weapons, dates back to early civilisation.

The subject of modern welding processes, such as those used in the manufacture of aero-space systems and components for the nuclear industry, involves a wide range of materials and complex structural design.

This book is mainly concerned with the most common material employed in the construction industry – carbon steel – and the theory is intended to run parallel with practical tuition through one of the many courses involved.

Questions will be found at the end of some chapters, and 165 Course specimen questions can be found in an Appendix at the end of the book.

May we wish you every success with your future in welding.

Stuart W. Gibson
Alan R. Smith

ACKNOWLEDGMENTS

The authors would particularly like to thank Len Gourd BSc, AIM, MITO, F.Weld.I. and Norman McConnell Sen.M.Weld.I. for their help and encouragement.

Also the following companies and organisations:

TWI, Cambridge; Hopwood Hall College, Rochdale; East Midlands Further Education Council, Nottingham; CENTRA, Manchester; The British Oxygen Company Ltd; BSI, Milton Keynes; Wescol Ltd; Co-Weld Liverpool Ltd; British Federal Ltd; Murex Welding Products Ltd; The ESAB Group; Signs and Labels Ltd and Frosts Auto Restoration Techniques Ltd, Rochdale.

Extracts from British Standards are reproduced with the permission of BSI. Complete copies can be obtained by post from BSI Sales, Linford Wood, Milton Keynes, MK14 6LE.

1 WHAT IS WELDING?

To weld means to join together. Welding is therefore a process of joining materials.

These days, many different types of materials can be welded together. However, in this book we will be looking at the joining of metals, and mainly the metal known as mild or low carbon steel. Because mild steel is the material most commonly used in the construction industry, it is usually the one chosen when learning about welding.

Many different materials need to be welded in modern industry, so there are a number of welding processes in use, some of which are very specialised. These other processes will be mentioned briefly in the text for interest. However, the main welding processes you will need to know about when starting welding are:

1 **Oxy-acetylene welding**, also known as **Gas welding**
   This process uses a flame from a blowpipe (chemical energy) to melt the edges of the metal parts to be joined together.
2 **Manual metal arc welding (MMA)**
3 **Tungsten arc gas-shielded welding (TAGS)**
4 **Metal arc gas-shielded welding (MAGS)**
   These three processes all use an electric arc (electrical energy) to melt the edges of the metal parts to be joined together.
5 **Resistance welding**
   This process uses the resistance heating effect of an electric current to melt the metals to be joined.

Each of these five processes has its own section in this book.

Welders can be skilled in one or more of the above processes, but these days, most welders have obtained competency levels in all five.

This may seem a lot to learn to begin with, but as you progress you will soon see that the skills learnt in one process transfer to another, and many points, such as safety, are common to all five.

✳ FOR INTEREST

Forge welding, the process of heating metals and hammering them together to form a joint, was practised thousands of years ago, particularly by the Egyptians.

Many knights' helmets were forge welded. The Black Prince's helmet was made from three pieces welded in such a way that the joints could not be seen.

What Items Are Welded?

The list of items that are welded is almost endless but includes ships, jet engines, rockets (including the space shuttle), cars, bridges, metal furniture, replacement hip joints, containers, and so on. Probably the smallest welded components are those used in electronic circuits. Some of the largest include ships and metal-framed buildings.

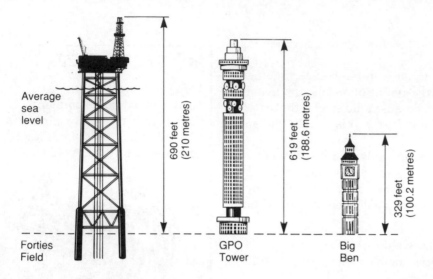

The sketch above shows just how big a welded oil platform is compared with two other well-known structures. What we tend to forget is just how much of the platform structure lies beneath the sea. The legs are often so large that a double decker bus could be driven through them.

Welding processes today have to produce high-quality joints that will withstand severe weather and loading conditions. Welds are tested by many sophisticated methods such as X-ray, gamma-ray and ultrasonic techniques (known as non-destructive testing). With the first two methods, engineers can actually 'see' inside the weld in much the same way that a doctor can see inside a patient when he uses an X-ray machine in hospital. Ultrasonic inspection passes high-frequency sound through the weld and surrounding metal, and the way the sound bounces back shows if the weld is acceptable.

Processes that melt the metals to form a weld are known as *fusion welding processes.*

Sometimes the edges of parts can be fused together by raising their temperature to melting point and allowing the molten metal to run into one weld.

An upturned edge weld is an example of this, where the edges of thin plate can be melted together by carefully passing either an oxy-acetylene flame or an electric arc along the joint at the correct speed. With this method, no extra metal is required.

In most cases, however, extra metal has to be added to the joint while it is still molten. This extra metal is known as *filler metal.*

Because of the intense heat involved in welding, various impurities can be formed by the reaction of atmospheric constituents and the surfaces of the metals being joined. If these impurities were not controlled in some way they could hinder the formation of the weld by preventing the metal from flowing properly. Inclusions inside the weld could also be formed, weakening the finished joint. Various methods are used to control these impurities and prevent atmospheric contamination of the weld.

In oxy-acetylene welding of mild steel, the flame acts as protection. This is explained in detail later in this book.

When oxy-acetylene welding other materials such as aluminium or stainless steel, a powdered chemical flux is used. A flux is also used when brazing. The flux is usually added to the rod by dipping its heated end into the powdered flux. This action is repeated when more flux is required. With manual metal arc welding, the rods are pre-coated with flux and are called *electrodes.*

In MAGS and TAGS welding, a gas shield is used. These gas shields are covered in detail within the MAGS and TAGS sections.

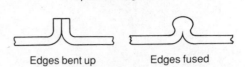

Upturned edge weld

Edges bent up   Edges fused

Welding is not always the best way of joining components. Sometimes the welder or welding engineer has to decide on other methods.

Many racing cars and competition motorcycles use brazing or bronze-welding in their construction, in addition to fusion welding. This technique allows a certain amount of flexibility or 'give' at the joints and this is what is sometimes required when a racing car corners very quickly or a motorcycle leaps over a bump.

Brazing and bronze-welding use a brass filler rod which melts at a lower temperature than the metals being joined. So, in this process, the metal has only to be heated to red-heat and the brass runs into the joint. In fusion welding, the metals being joined, as well as the filler material, would have to be melted.

A powdered flux is required for brazing and bronze-welding. The chemical flux helps clean the work surfaces and allows the brass to run freely.

4

2 | HEALTH AND SAFETY

The majority of the points in this section are common to all welding processes and welding workshops.

The Health and Safety at Work etc. Act 1974

This Act is very important as it covers the Legal duties of employers, employees and self-employed persons.

Because Health and Safety are the responsibility of all, one of the important objectives of the Act is to encourage employers and employees to work together to make a safer workplace.

General Duties of Employers

The following points are summarised from the Act:

1. It is the duty of every employee to ensure the safety, health and welfare of all employees at the workplace. This includes the maintenance of plant and the working environment, and also the provision of safe entrances to and exits from the workplace.
2. Safety and the absence of risks to health must be ensured during all handling, storage and transportation operations.
3. Instruction, training and supervision must be provided so far as is reasonably practicable.
4. A written statement of the general policy with respect to health and safety of employees at work must be drawn up.
5. Provision is also included in the Act for the election of employees as safety representatives.

General Duties of Employees

As an employee it is your duty to take reasonable care of your own health and safety. You must not take risks or endanger others by your actions. You must also co-operate with the employer on health and safety matters.

Control of Substances Hazardous to Health Regulations 1988 (COSHH)

Under these regulations an assessment of substances used in the workplace must be undertaken. The assessment should include:

1. Listing substances used in the workplace;
2. Stating the possible harmful effects of these substances;
3. Noting where the substances are used, handled and stored;
4. Assessing who might be exposed to them and the length of exposure involved;
5. Looking at ways of preventing or controlling such exposure.

Some Common Hazard Signs

In welding, there are various special hazards, such as fumes and radiation from manual metal arc welding operations. Anyone who might come into contact with hazardous substances must be told about the assessment.

The next few pages on safety precautions for welding are based on The Health and Safety at Work etc. Act and the control measures listed by COSHH.

The COSHH control measures to limit or prevent exposure are:

1. Substitute the substance with a safer alternative;
2. Introduce technical or engineering methods of controlling exposure;
3. Reduce exposure by following the safe systems of work.

If these methods do not give adequate control, then, in addition, *suitable* protective clothing should be provided.

Welding Safety Precautions

Fusion welding and cutting processes involve intense heat, either from an electric arc or a gas flame. In this section we look at ways of protecting the body from this heat and minimising discomfort so that high-quality welding can be undertaken.

In the arc welding processes, rays are given off which are high in infra-red and ultra-violet emissions. If you looked at an arc without proper eye protection, you would get what is called *'arc eye'*. This is a painful condition causing irritation of the eyes, which can last for up to forty-eight hours in severe cases.

Protection of Eyes Regulations 1974 – Schedule No. 1, Process No. 24

CLASS 3
When fitted, recommended Filters for Electric Arc Welding to BS 679
Usage:

Welding process range of	Approximate required welding current (in amps)	Filter(s)
Metal arc welding (coated electrodes) Continuous covered-electrode welding Carbon dioxide shielded continuous covered-electrode welding	Up to 100	8/EW 9/EW
	100–300	10/EW 11/EW
	Over 300	12/EW 13/EW 14/EW
Metal arc welding (bare wire) Carbon arc welding Inert gas metal arc welding Atomic hydrogen welding	Up to 200	10/EW 11/EW
	Over 200	12/EW 13/EW 14/EW
Automatic carbon dioxide shielded metal arc welding (bare wire)	OVER 500	15/EW 16/EW
Inert gas tungsten arc welding	UP TO 15	8/EW
	15–75	9/EW
	75–100	10/EW
	100–200	11/EW
	200–250	12/EW
	250–300	13/EW 14/EW

CLASS 4
As above, fitted auxiliary heat absorbing filter

Where two or more shade numbers are recommended for a particular process and current range, the higher shade numbers should be used for welding in dark surroundings and the lower shade numbers for welding in bright daylight.

Anyone with this condition should seek medical advice, as eye drops that will ease the pain are available.

The welder's eyes and face must therefore be protected from these rays and also the intense heat and light rays coming from the arc. The shield should cover the sides of the face and have a special filter lens (like a very strong sun glass), which is made to British Standard 679 specification.

A list of recommended filters is given in the table. The number increases as the filter becomes more powerful. The letters 'EW' stand for Electric Welding.

Handshield

Types of Welding Shield

The arc welder can choose which type of shield to use for particular applications. The handshield is probably less tiring and in some cases easier to use, but gives less protection to the head.

When welding overhead, (a skill which requires a certain amount of practice), a leather cap is also worn. For work inside aluminium or stainless steel fabrications, protection to the back of the head and neck may also be required to protect these areas from reflected rays.

The filter glass of the shield is protected by a plain cover glass which should be kept clean and replaced when spatter damage (small particles of molten metal given off from the welding operation) makes it difficult to see through.

Some shields allow the filter to be lifted while still leaving the clear glass in position. This allows burnt flux (which is called slag) to be chipped off from the weld while still giving eye protection.

Helmet or Headshield

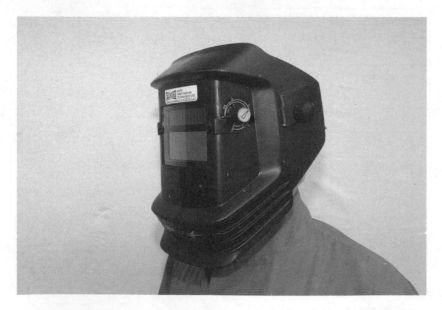

One of the latest types of solar-powered welding masks with light-reactive lens that automatically adjusts to the correct shade of filter according to the arc intensity. The adjustment time is two milliseconds. The lens instantly clears when welding stops to allow protection with good visibility for slag removal or repositioning of work. (Courtesy of Frost Auto Restoration Techniques Ltd, Rochdale)

8

Protection against Burns from Sparks, Hot Metal Arcs and Flames

For general welding, a leather apron is usually worn over the top of overalls. For heavy-duty welding, spats can be worn over the top of industrial boots to protect the feet from particles of hot metal and sparks. Leather gloves afford protection during normal operations and can be supplemented with leather sleeves for heavier work. Heavy-duty gauntlets are also made.

For gas welding, it is not usually necessary to wear a helmet like the ones used for electric arc welding. Goggles manufactured in accordance with BS679 are satisfactory in protecting the eyes from sparks, heat and light radiated from the work. Gas welding goggles are made in different styles, and various types are available for wearing over spectacles if required.

Goggles are provided with a filter glass to BS679, and a protective cover glass. The cover glasses should be cleaned as required, and replaced when they are damaged to such an extent that they obscure vision.

Gas welding goggles

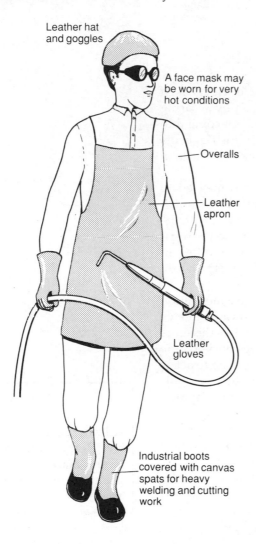

Leather hat and goggles

A face mask may be worn for very hot conditions

Overalls

Leather apron

Leather gloves

Industrial boots covered with canvas spats for heavy welding and cutting work

---

! ! REMEMBER

Leather gloves are not made for picking up hot metal – they are designed to protect the hands from heat and sparks when welding.

Precautions to be Taken to Avoid Electric Shocks

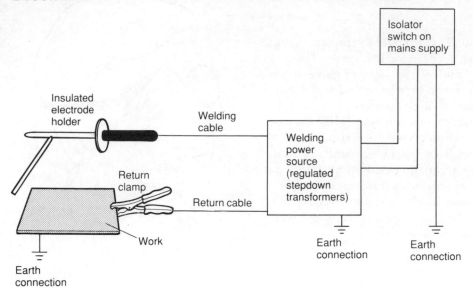

Block diagram of an alternating current welding circuit showing earth connections.

Damp and wet conditions greatly increase the severity of an electric shock, if a live conductor is touched. Care should therefore be taken by wearing gloves when changing electrodes so that the bare hands do not come into contact with welding terminals. The wearing of thick soled industrial boots and standing on dry boards are further precautions against electric shock in damp conditions.

All metal casings on electrical equipment should also be connected to earth in order to give a safe discharge of electricity should there be a malfunction and a live conductor inside accidentally comes into contact with the case. Good earth connections are essential, because if they are poor, the resistance to the path of electricity will be high and the current could follow an easier path to earth through the human body if the live metal part is touched, causing electrocution.

In large fabrication shops, several people may be working on a fabrication at one time. There may be people welding, drilling holes, marking out etc., and there may be several pieces of electrical equipment in use. It is therefore of vital importance that the work is earthed. Most companies bury a large cast iron or copper plate about 1½ metres square and 2 metres deep to act as the earth. Cables are carried through steel conduit within a factory, and this conduit is connected to the earthing plate or plates, so that should any part become live it will immediately discharge to earth.

In the case of welding transformers, an extra earthing wire connects the metal parts of the equipment to the main earthing system. This extra earth is sometimes included in the supply cable.

All electrical equipment should be regularly checked and maintained by qualified personnel, and any damaged equipment should be clearly labelled as such and taken out of service until repairs can be undertaken.

> △ **SAFETY**
>
> **All emergency switches for electrical equipment should be clearly marked and located in positions that are easily accessible.**

Precautions to be Taken to Avoid the Risk of Fire and Explosion

These risks are greatest with gas welding and cutting, and anyone contemplating carrying out these operations is strongly recommended to obtain and read the publications of the Health and Safety Executive. These are:

Booklet 32. Repair of Drums and Small Tanks: Explosion and Fire Risk
and
Booklet 50. Welding and Flame-cutting using Compressed Gases

Both booklets are obtainable from Her Majesty's Stationery Office.
A summary of the main safety precautions is included in this section, and details of safe working and mechanical protection devices appear in the Gas welding section.

It cannot be stressed too strongly that both the gases most commonly employed for gas welding must be treated with care and respect.

Acetylene, for example, is a potentially explosive mixture with air within the range of 2 to 82 per cent of acetylene. It will be appreciated that such a range could be achieved merely from leakage or escape. For this reason, it is essential that all gas welding equipment is well maintained.

Oxygen is non-flammable but will support and increase combustion in flammable materials. It is very important that the atmosphere does not become enriched with oxygen, say from a leaking hose or pipe, as the slightest spark under these conditions can cause a 'flash' fire in which everything flammable in the area is burnt in a matter of seconds.

Oxygen can ignite oil, so it is very important that the workshop and working clothes are clean.

All the fusion welding processes produce sparks and hot metal, so it is of vital importance that any materials likely to catch fire are moved well away from welding operations and fire extinguishers should be sited at convenient locations.

It must be remembered that entire factories have been destroyed by fires arising from unattended hot metal or sparks from welding and cutting processes.

All emergency exits should be clear of obstructions on both sides. They should be clearly marked with exit signs and well maintained for ease of operation.

Using and Storing Cylinders of Compressed Gas

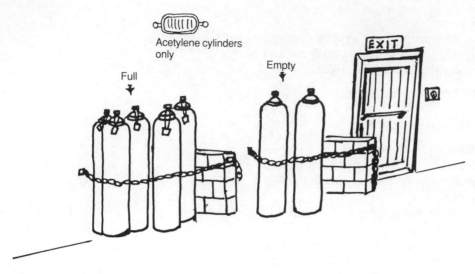

The store room should be well ventilated, fire-proof and fitted with flame-proof electrical fittings. Full and empty cylinders should be kept apart from each other in clearly marked storage areas.

Summary of Main Safety Precautions to be Taken When Using and Storing Cylinders of Compressed Gas

1. Full and empty cylinders should be kept apart from each other in clearly marked storage areas. The storage room should be fire-proof and have flame-proof electrical fittings. The room should be well ventilated.
2. Never smoke, wear oily or greasy clothing or allow exposed flames in the storage room.
3. In storage and in use, cylinders should always be protected from snow and ice and also from the direct rays of the sun.
4. Acetylene cylinders should always be kept in an upright position.
5. Oxygen and combustible gases such as acetylene and propane should not be stored together.
6. Cylinders must be kept away from heat, grease and oil. Heat will increase the pressure of the gas and can weaken the cylinder wall, while oil and grease can ignite spontaneously in the presence of pure oxygen.
7. Use a cylinder trolley to transport cylinders, in order to avoid any damage which could otherwise occur by dropping or bumping cylinders violently together. Always handle cylinders with care.
8. In use, always protect cylinders from the sparks and flames of welding and cutting operations, and ensure that they are clear of electrical apparatus where they may be a danger of stray arcing taking place.
9. Never test for leaks with a naked flame – use soapy water.
10. Always shut off the gas supply when the cylinders are not in use, even for a short time, and particularly when transporting cylinders. Don't overtighten the valve when shutting off the cylinder, just tighten it enough to prevent any leakage.
11. Copper or copper alloy fittings with more than 70 per cent of copper should *never* be used, because copper can form an explosive compound called copper acetylide when in contact with acetylene.

12. Blow out the cylinder outlet by quickly opening and closing the cylinder valve to clear out any dirt or dust, before fitting the regulator. Do not use oil or grease on valves or gas welding equipment. Equipment should be checked before and after use and serviced at regular intervals.
13. Always ensure that cylinders are secure and will not fall over either in use or in storage.
14. Should a cylinder spindle valve become frozen, thaw it out slowly with warm water, *never* with a flame.
15. If an acetylene cylinder becomes heated for any reason, immediately take it outside, and immerse it in water or spray it with water. Open the valve and keep it as cool as possible until the cylinder is empty. Then inform the cylinder suppliers.

Know Your Fire Extinguisher Colour Code

Fire extinguisher type	Colour code	Suitable for use with	Comment
Water	Red	Wood, paper, textiles etc.	Unsafe on all electrical equipment at all voltages
Dry powder	Blue	Flammable liquids, high voltages	Safe on high voltages
Foam	Green	Flammable liquids	Unsafe on all electrical equipment at all voltages
Carbon dioxide (CO_2)	Black	Flammable liquids, high voltages	Safe on high voltages
Vaporising liquids	Green	Flammable liquids, high voltages	Safe on high voltages

The Need for Adequate Ventilation and Fume Extraction when Welding

This section looks at some of the main methods and considerations involved in the control of fumes in a general workshop where welding is taking place on mild steel.

Because all fumes should be treated as being potentially hazardous, they are covered by the COSHH regulations and those of the Joint European Directive. This means that an assessment must be made of the potential hazards involved in the welding of different materials and the COSHH control measures put into force.

This is of vital importance, as certain fumes can be fatal.

When welding mild steel, the fumes are not usually injurious **if correct precautions are observed.**

Particular care and specific control measures have to be taken when using electrode coatings containing fluorides, that is, low hydrogen electrodes and the welding of monel, nickel and stainless steels or any metal with a high chromium content.

When welding or cutting materials which have been painted, brass and galvanised or cadmium plated metals, the work should be carried out in a well-ventilated area with fume extraction at the point of work. The COSHH assessment in such cases may also advise the use of a respirator as well.

If a welder is exposed to a source of fumes, medical assistance should be sought immediately.

Further Considerations

Vapours from Degreasing Operations

These are particularly dangerous where welding operations are concerned, as many decompose by the action of ultra-violet radiation given off from the arc and will form phosgene or other poisonous gases.

For this reason, degreasing operations using trichlorethylene or similar solvents should not be carried out anywhere near welding operations, to prevent the vapours being drawn into the area near the arc. Any work which has been degreased using solvents should be completely dry and free from solvent residue before welding is commenced.

Gases Produced by the Action of the Arc and Heat

Gases are formed when fluxes burn and decompose and by the effects of ultra-violet and infra-red radiation on air. The ultra-violet light from an arc can cause the oxygen in air to change into the molecular form and become ozone. Ozone is very chemically active and, if inhaled, can produce severe irritation and a loss of lung capacity. Ozone is the only gas in a welding atmosphere that can be filtered out, as it changes back to oxygen on contact with solids.

Nitrogen oxides can be formed by the action of heat and ultra-violet radiation. These oxides can irritate the lungs and in high concentrations can cause cyanosis (a blue colouration caused by lack of oxygen in the blood). This condition can be fatal. A further toxic gas found in welding is carbon monoxide, which is poisonous in high concentrations.

Most other gases met with in welding have a low toxicity. But it must be remembered that any gas can replace air in the environment. The shielding

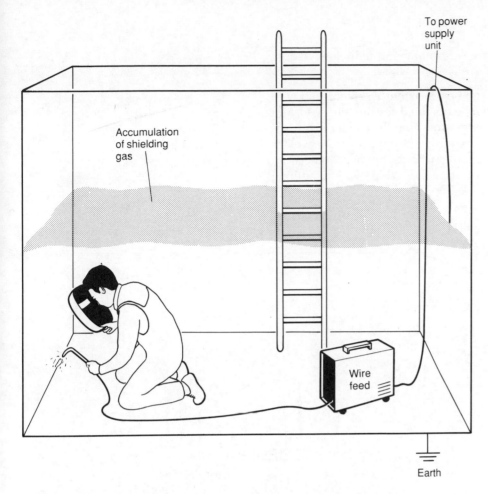

To power
supply
unit

Accumulation
of shielding
gas

Wire
feed

Earth

*Sketch showing build-up of asphyxiating shielding gas due to lack of adequate ventilation and
air replenishment.* **This is a very dangerous situation**

gases used in TAGS and MAGS welding will displace air and in a confined
space there is a risk of asphyxiation if air is not replenished at the same rate
that the diluted atmosphere is extracted.

Argon and carbon dioxide, both widely used shielding gases, being heavier than air can settle at floor level, and if not extracted can build up into a
stagnant blanket of asphyxiating gases. An extractor duct at floor level and a
fan-blower replenishing fresh air into the confined area will avoid this situation. Any extracted fumes, which will usually contain nitrogen oxides,
should be discharged in such a way that they do not contaminate other work
areas.

Methods of Fume Extraction

Basically, there are three main methods of controlling and reducing welding fume levels.

1. Atmosphere in the welder's helmet can be consistently replenished with fresh air. Special welding helmets can be obtained for this purpose, and these probably provide the best answer in protecting the welder in normal situations. Full breathing apparatus may also be worn by the welder underneath the helmet, when working in particularly hazardous situations. Both of these methods, while protecting the welder, will do nothing to prevent the fume build-up in the workshop.

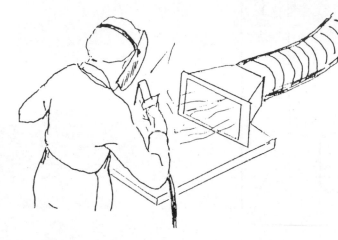

Local extraction of welding fumes

2. Small extractor ducts which can be placed in the vicinity of the welding operation can be very effective, as they extract the fumes at source. In practice, however, these ducts require to be moved frequently in order to keep them close to the welding operation and thus working at maximum efficiency.

   Correct use of these small extractors will make a marked reduction to the level of fumes in the surrounding atmosphere.

3. Roof extractor hoods will help keep the overall fumes in a workshop down to an acceptable level. However, if the fumes go directly outside, together with large quantities of air, this can cause problems when heating a workshop in the winter months. For this reason, systems which recirculate the extracted air through filters can be installed, and such systems, although more expensive to install, will soon pay for themselves with savings in heating costs.

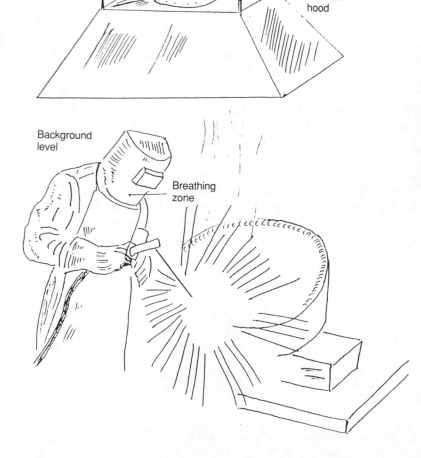

Fume extractor hood

Background level

Breathing zone

How Fume Levels are Measured

The fumes produced by welding and cutting operations can be carried into the zone around the welder's head by convection currents of hot air rising from the work, or even by badly sited extraction equipment. The chemical composition of the fumes will determine to what extent the substances constitute a health hazard.

The maximum level for each chemical compound to which a welder can be exposed is specified as the Occupational Exposure Limit or OEL. Every year, the Health and Safety Executive in the United Kingdom publishes a list giving the OELs for the substances commonly found in industrial atmospheres. These limits give a basis from which the acceptability of a working atmosphere can be determined.

It is usual to take measurements of the atmosphere in two main areas, these being the breathing zone, which represents the breathing atmosphere of the welder and will probably have the highest level of fume concentration as it is close to the welding operation, and the background atmosphere. An analysis of the background levels is important when considering if it is safe for other people to work in the surrounding area while welding is taking place.

Fume content is measured by drawing a known volume of air through a filter. The fumes are then analysed chemically, the total amount being calculated in milligrams of fumes per cubic metre of air, and the relative amounts of individual compounds compared with the relevant Occupational Exposure Limits.

When welding outdoors, there is normally enough natural air movement to disperse the welding fumes, but in a normal factory, even though there may be some air movement in the workshop, fumes can collect near the ceiling if there is not adequate extraction.

Good fume extraction is essential when welding in a confined space, such as inside a tank, as the fume level can quickly exceed the recommended limits in such circumstances.

Example of local fume extraction when manual metal arc welding. (Courtesy of TWI, Cambridge)

3 | OXY-ACETYLENE WELDING

Oxy-acetylene welding is known as *gas welding*. There are two systems used for gas welding. These are known as the *high-pressure system* and the *low-pressure system*.

The high-pressure system uses acetylene in cylinders. The low-pressure system uses acetylene produced on the premises in an acetylene generator. As the name implies, this acetylene is at a lower pressure than the cylinder acetylene and the equipment involves special safety precautions and a blow-pipe which has an injector system to allow the low-pressure acetylene to be sucked through by the higher-pressure oxygen.

Because the *high-pressure* system is the most widely used and therefore the one that you are most likely to learn welding on, these notes concentrate mainly on this system.

Equipment for High-pressure Systems

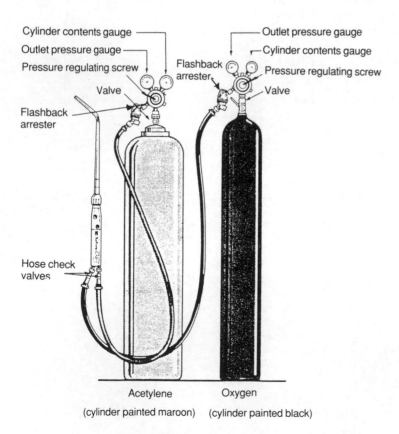

Cylinder contents gauge
Outlet pressure gauge
Pressure regulating screw
Valve
Flashback arrester
Hose check valves

Outlet pressure gauge
Cylinder contents gauge
Flashback arrester
Pressure regulating screw
Valve

Acetylene
(cylinder painted maroon)

Oxygen
(cylinder painted black)

High-pressure welding outfit

> *Why oxy-acetylene?* These gases are used because they provide a flame with the highest temperature (approximately 3,250°C at a point just in front of the flame's inner cone)

Acetylene

For the high-pressure welding system, acetylene gas is stored in steel cylinders which are colour-coded maroon.

Acetylene is, however, unstable when under pressure. Because of this fact, when stored in cylinders it is dissolved in a chemical called acetone. For this reason it is called 'dissolved acetylene'.

A porous material such as charcoal, synthetic asbestos or kapok is also placed inside the cylinder and divides the available space for the dissolved acetylene into a large number of small cells. This dispersal can prevent the sudden decomposition of the acetylene through the whole cylinder should accidental local heating occur. It can therefore help to prevent an explosion.

At room temperature and normal atmospheric pressure, acetone liquid will dissolve about 25 times its own volume of acetylene. If the pressure is increased to 15 bar, this value is increased to approximately 375 times its own volume.

A full acetylene cylinder is pressurised to 15 bar and will contain either between 5.7 m^3 or 8.6 m^3 of acetylene gas, depending on the size of the cylinder.

Larger demands for acetylene can be met by using a manifold system, where several cylinders are coupled together.

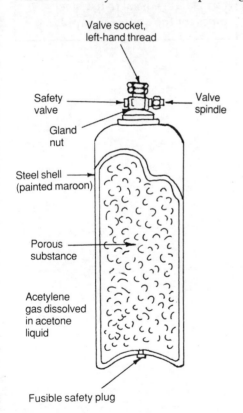

Valve socket, left-hand thread

Safety valve

Valve spindle

Gland nut

Steel shell (painted maroon)

Porous substance

Acetylene gas dissolved in acetone liquid

Fusible safety plug

Cut-away view of acetylene cylinder

Manifold Systems

(Used for larger workshops when a single cylinder will not suffice.)

The method used to connect cylinders in a manifold system is by the use of 'pigtail' pipes. The main pipe then takes the gas to the line regulators and welding stations. Manifold systems must always be installed by professional suppliers.

---

* SAFETY

Pipes for acetylene must not be made out of copper, as this would cause an explosive compound known as copper acetylide to be formed. It is usual to use steel pipes for the acetylene supply.

Method of Determining the Amount of Acetylene in a Cylinder

Because the acetylene is in the dissolved condition, the amount in a cylinder cannot be determined accurately from the pressure gauge reading. The most accurate method of determining the quantity of gas in a cylinder is therefore to weigh it, and subtract this weight from that of a full cylinder. (The weight of a full cylinder is usually given on the label.) The volume of gas can then be calculated taking 1 litre of acetylene gas to weigh 1.1 g.

Acetylene should not be drawn from a cylinder at a rate of more than $\frac{1}{5}$th of its capacity per hour. If this rate is exceeded, high amounts of acetone can be found in the gas.

Oxygen

Oxygen for welding is supplied in solid drawn steel cylinders which are painted black and are charged to a pressure of 173.5 bar (2,500 lb/sq.in.).

The volume of oxygen contained in a cylinder is approximately proportional to the pressure, so that for every 10 litres of oxygen consumed, the pressure will fall by about 0.02 N/mm². Because of this fact, we can use a contents gauge to show how much oxygen remains in the cylinder. The valve at the top of the oxygen cylinder has a right-handed screw thread to allow for the connection of the oxygen regulator.

If large quantities of oxygen are required, several cylinders can be coupled together in a *manifold* system and this can give the required volume of flow rate. When consumption is very high, oxygen can be supplied and stored in liquid form. This requires a special installation and particular codes of practice.

Gas Pressure Regulators

Pressure regulators for welding have a high-pressure gauge, which indicates the pressure of gas in the cylinder, and a low-pressure gauge, which indicates the pressure set by the regulator valve for the required welding pressure. With single-stage regulators, the high pressure from the cylinder is reduced in a single stage to the required welding pressure. There is greater accuracy and less likelihood of fluctuating welding gas pressure if a two-stage regulator is used. With this type of regulator, the high pressure is reduced in two stages down to the welding pressure to be delivered to the blowpipe.

The colour band on an oxygen regulator is blue and on an acetylene regulator it is maroon or red.

The cylinder and hose connections on the oxygen regulator have right-hand threads whereas they are left-handed on the acetylene regulator. The acetylene connection nuts have chamfers or grooves cut in them to indicate that they are left-hand threaded.

The outlet gauge on the oxygen regulator reads up to 4.8 bar. The outlet gauge on the acetylene regulator reads up to 1 bar.

The high-pressure or inlet gauge on the oxygen regulator reads up to 100 bar. The inlet gauge on the acetylene regulator reads up to 8 bar.

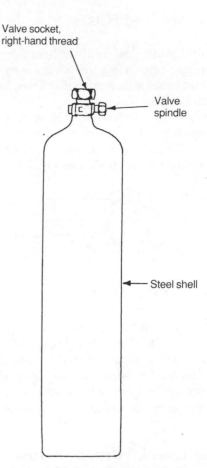

Oxygen cylinder – colour code black

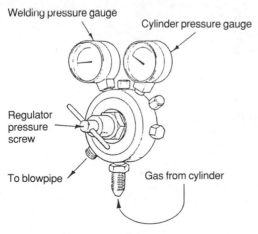

Pressure regulator

Gas Welding Hoses

High-pressure gas welding hoses are made with a neoprene lining and cover, and consist of three layers of rubberised canvas. This gives abrasion-resistant hoses which are light in weight. They are colour-coded blue for oxygen and red for fuel gas.

The lengths are from 5 to 20 metres, with bore diameters of 4.5 mm for a maximum working pressure of 7 bar and 8 mm for a maximum working pressure of 12 bar. Bore diameters of 10 mm are available for a maximum working pressure of 15 bar. BS 924 J and BS 796 J cover hoses for welding and cutting.

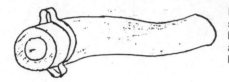

High-pressure hose secured to connectors by 'O' clips which are 'closed' by long-nosed pliers

Hose Connectors

Connectors of the nipple and nut type are available for each type of hose with 6.4 mm ($\frac{1}{4}$ in. BSP) and 10 mm ($\frac{3}{8}$ in. BSP) nuts. These brass fittings are used to connect the welding or cutting hose to the regulator or flashback arrestor. 'O'-clips are used to secure them to the hose. Again, to save any confusion, all nuts for the fuel gas line are grooved and have left-hand threads, while the nuts for use on the oxygen line are smooth and have right-hand threads.

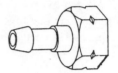

Grooved nut connector with left-hand thread for combustible gas

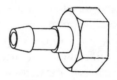

Plain nut connector with right-hand thread for non-combustible gas

Hose Check Valves or Hose Protectors

Hose check valves are an automatic safety device incorporating a spring-loaded non-return valve. Their purpose is to prevent oxygen and fuel gases mixing in the hoses. The valves stop the backfeeding by which the oxygen would contaminate the fuel gas hose or vice-versa. This ensures that welding and cutting equipment is protected against backfeeding which can cause extensive damage to hoses and regulators should a flashback occur.

Hose check valves prevent the feed-back of gases from regions of higher or lower pressures and reduce the risk of a flashback from a partially or totally blocked nozzle or a leaking blowpipe valve etc.

Hose check valves should be connected between the blowpipe and each hose. The connection at the blowpipe is by a left-hand threaded nut for acetylene and a right-hand threaded nut connector for the oxygen supply. They are fastened to the hoses by 'O'-clips.

Although the check valves will prevent a backfire from damaging the hoses and can reduce the risk of a flashback, they will not stop a flashback. In order to have full protection against the dangers of a flashback, arrestors must be fitted.

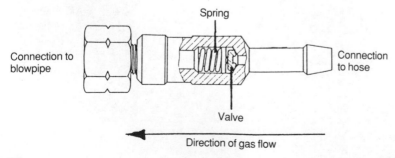

Spring

Connection to blowpipe

Connection to hose

Valve

Direction of gas flow

Hose check valve/protector, containing a spring-loaded valve which will seal off the line should a backflow occur.

Flame Traps (Flashback Arrestors)

In gas welding and cutting equipment, flame traps give protection to operators and equipment against the hazard of mixed gas explosions. The explosion or flashback can occur when backfeeding of gases takes place. A mixture of gases is then present in either the oxygen or fuel gas hose. Flame traps are designed to arrest the most severe forms of flashback under all operating conditions and should carry full Health and Safety Inspectorate approval for operation within the recommended working pressures specified for each model. It is recommended that approved flame traps are installed in both oxygen and fuel gas lines immediately downstream of the pressure regulator.

Flame trap. (Courtesy of Murex Welding Products Ltd)

High-pressure and Low-pressure Blowpipes for Welding and Cutting

The High-pressure Blowpipe

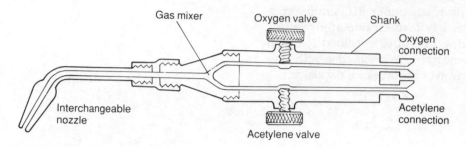

Principle of the high-pressure blowpipe

The high-pressure blowpipe is simply a mixing chamber, with regulating valves to vary the pressure of gases as required.

A selection of nozzles is supplied with the blowpipe. These have orifices of varying sizes (see Welding Data Charts), and each is stamped with a number, usually indicating the consumption of gas in cubic feet or litres per hour depending on the make.

These nozzles will cover a range of welding requirements from thin sheet to heavy-duty welding.

The above sketch shows a simple cross-sectional view of a high-pressure blowpipe. It can be seen that the oxygen and acetylene enter the blowpipe through separate connections and then mix in the gas mixer, arriving at the nozzle in approximately equal volumes.

A high-pressure blowpipe *must not* be used on a low-pressure system.

The Low-pressure Blowpipe

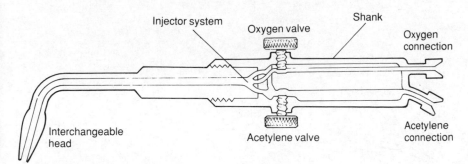

Principle of the low-pressure blowpipe

The low-pressure blowpipe contains an injector system. The high-pressure oxygen travels through the injector and draws the low-pressure acetylene into the mixing chamber, giving it sufficient velocity to maintain a steady flame. The injector will also help to prevent backfiring.

It is usual for the whole head to be interchangeable with this type of blowpipe, as the head contains both the nozzle and the injector.

The interchangeable head is necessary as the injector size will vary for each nozzle size.

The low-pressure welding blowpipe is more expensive than the high-pressure type. It can be used on the high-pressure system, but its use has fallen over the last few years compared with the high-pressure blowpipe and high-pressure system.

The Gas Economizer

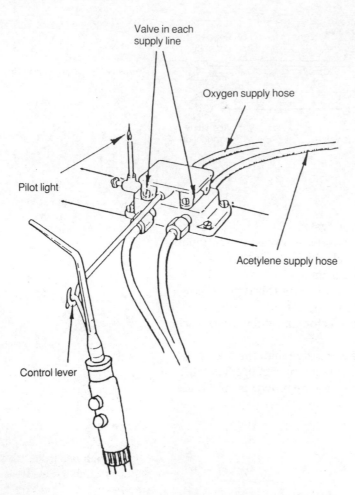

Valve in each supply line

Oxygen supply hose

Pilot light

Acetylene supply hose

Control lever

The gas economizer is a very useful item of equipment designed for use with pipeline distribution of oxygen and acetylene to welding points.

The economizer uses two valves which are normally held open by a spring, but will be closed by the weight of a blowpipe hung on the control lever arm.

Oxygen and acetylene supplies are coupled to the inlet side of the fitting, the gas hoses to the blowpipe being coupled to the outlet side. When the blowpipe is lifted off the arm, the gases may be ignited at the pilot light, and the flame adjusted to the correct setting in the normal way. Between welding operations, the blowpipe is hung on the arm, shutting off the gases. When the blowpipe is needed again, the flame can be lit from the pilot and welding started without loss of time or gas needed to adjust the flame.

Installing gas economizers can reduce gas consumption by as much as 20 per cent, when the average amount of gas wasted while the flame is being adjusted and during the time the blowpipe is laid aside with the flame burning (while a job is being changed or adjusted) is taken into account.

If a blowpipe is not going to be used for some time, then it should be shut down completely. The economizer is designed for use when there are only short intervals of time between welding operations.

Using the Gas Welding Equipment

When assembling equipment, never use oil or grease as these substances can ignite causing an explosion. Soapy water can ease a thread and will also indicate if there is a leak. Any connections that do not assemble easily need to be replaced, but remember that acetylene fitments have left-hand threads and oxygen fitments have right-hand threads!

Before opening the cylinder valves check:

1. Hoses for burns or cuts which may leak.
2. All connections for tightness.
3. That the regulator pressure valve is off (loose).
4. That both blowpipe valves are closed.

The cylinder valves should be opened just half a turn using the valve spindle key.

When shutting down equipment check:

1. That the cylinder valves are shut off:
2. That the hoses have been emptied of oxygen and acetylene, by opening the blowpipe valves until the welding pressure gauge indicates zero and then closing both blowpipe valves. ·
3. Turn off the regulator valve (loosen the pressure adjusting screw).

Smaller cylinders are available allowing greater portability. (Courtesy Murex Welding Products Ltd)

⚠ SAFETY

Backfires and flashbacks

When you begin your welding training, you will be told about two occurrences of which you should be wary.

The first of these is the *backfire*. This is the flame snapping back inside the blowpipe or nozzle. As a rule, the flame quickly extinguishes itself. This condition is not uncommon and neither is it serious. It is generally caused by insufficient pressure, dirt in the nozzle or some other blockage. You will learn more about the various causes when you begin your practical welding. However, whenever you get a backfire you should always turn off the gases at the cylinder valve – acetylene first, then oxygen – and investigate the cause. (Sometimes the nozzle simply requires cleaning with nozzle reamers; these are small reamers specially made for the purpose.)

More serious than the backfire is the flashback. A flashback is a *backfire* which has gone back to the hoses. Such a condition, if not attended to correctly, can become extremely dangerous and may even lead to an explosion.

A flashback starts as a backfire, so this is why you must turn off the gas at the cylinder valves as soon as a backfire occurs. In order for it not to develop into a flashback.

There are various safety devices on the equipment. Such as one-way valves where the hoses connect to the blowpipe, and flashback arrestors where the hoses connect to the regulators. Regulators are also valves, and the equipment is fitted with a main cylinder valve. With these devices, oxy-acetylene welding is made much safer, but the biggest safety factor of all is **the operator turning off the cylinder valves quickly when there is any doubt.**

Lighting the Blowpipe

To light the blowpipe, the regulators are set to the recommended pressures (this is first done under the supervision of a skilled welder, until you have got the procedure perfected). When the regulators are set correctly, you should first turn on the acetylene valve on the blowpipe, and light the acetylene at the nozzle with a spark lighter (a match is not recommended). At first the flame will be yellow and smoky. The soot and smoke being given off is carbon, because combustion is incomplete owing to the shortage of oxygen in the flame. The yellow flame is either increased or decreased until the black smoke reduces and then finally disappears. This is done by using the acetylene valve on the blowpipe. In this condition, the acetylene supply is right for the particular size of nozzle.

At this point, the oxygen is turned on at the blowpipe valve. As the pressure of the oxygen is increased, the flame gradually takes on the appearance of the *neutral flame*, with a small blue inner cone and larger outer envelope. If there is a feathery white plume around the inner cone, this is the carburising flame, and indicates that a little more oxygen is required to obtain the neutral flame.

If the inner cone is small and tapered, this indicates that there is too much oxygen. This flame is called the *oxidising flame* and requires the oxygen to be reduced slightly at the blowpipe valve in order to obtain the neutral flame.

The three different types of gas welding flame and their uses are shown below.

The three different types of gas welding flame

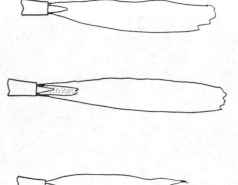

1. *Neutral flame:* This flame burns equal quantities of oxygen and acetylene.

2. *Carburising flame:* This flame has an excess of acetylene which gives a carbon-rich zone around the inner cone. It is used for hardsurfacing.

3. *Oxidising flame:* This flame has an excess of oxygen which results in an oxygen-rich zone just beyond the cone. It is used for brazing and bronze welding.

When you have mastered the technique of lighting the blowpipe and correctly adjusting the neutral flame you will be ready to practise the leftward technique of gas welding.

This will usually involve some practice, under supervision, on scrap pieces of material.

The first stage is to deposit a straight bead of weld on a single piece of material and then, when this is perfected, to practise joining two pieces.

The ultimate aim is to achieve a standard of weld quality to enable you to produce the required test pieces if you intend becoming a qualified welder.

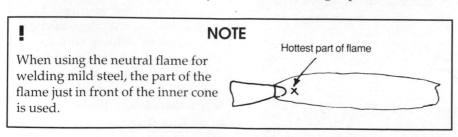

! **NOTE**

When using the neutral flame for welding mild steel, the part of the flame just in front of the inner cone is used.

Hottest part of flame

The Leftward and Forward Technique of Gas Welding

Filler rod

80–90°

Nozzle

30–40°

60–70°

Weld

Parent plate

Direction of travel

Nozzle

Filler rod

Tacks (small welds are used to hold plates in position)

(Bevel not required for thin sheet)

The leftward method of gas welding is used for welding steel plate up to 5 mm in thickness. It can also be used for welding non-ferrous metals.

When the blowpipe is held in the right hand, the weld travels from right to left, with the filler rod in front of the nozzle.

The inner cone of the flame, which should be in the neutral condition for welding mild steel, is held close to the metal but not touching it.

For the best welding conditions, the blowpipe and filler rod should be held at approximately those angles shown in the sketch. The nozzle is given either circular or slight side-to-side movements in order to obtain good and even fusion at the sides of the weld.

To commence welding by this technique, the flame is played on the start of the joint until a molten pool is formed. The welding then proceeds by filler rod being fed or dipped into the molten pool. The rod is melted by this dipping action and not by the flame itself.

The filler rod should not be held continuously in the molten pool, as this could prevent the heat of the flame and thus the molten pool from reaching the lower parts of the weld joint, resulting in possible lack of fusion.

The correct technique is to dip the rod in and out of the pool at regular intervals as the weld proceeds. The frequency of this action will be determined by the size of the weld being deposited and the correct action improves with practice.

Car wing repair set-up ready for welding by oxy-acetylene technique. (Courtesy of Frost Auto Restoration Techniques Ltd, Rochdale)

29

Examples of BS4872 Test Pieces

(These test pieces are used as end tests on some basic welding courses)

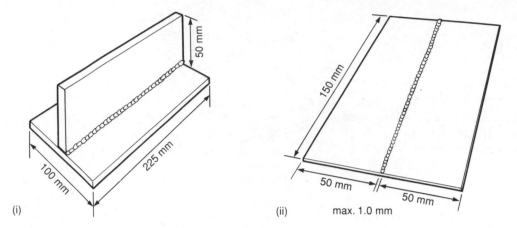

(i)

(ii)   max. 1.0 mm

(i) Tee fillet weld in the horizontal position on steel 3 mm thick.
(ii) Square edge butt weld in the flat position on steel 1.5 mm thick.

Both welds to be tested in accordance with BS4872 criteria.

Typical Nozzle Sizes and Gas Pressures for Oxy-Acetylene Welding

(Manufacturers' information should always be consulted as information can vary slightly with different makes of blowpipe)

Mild steel thickness		Nozzle size		Operating pressures				Consumption of gas			
				Acetylene		Oxygen		Acetylene		Oxygen	
(mm)	(in.)	(swg)		(bar)	(lb/in.²)	(bar)	(lb/in.²)	(l/h)	(ft³/h)	(l/h)	(ft³/h)
0.9	–	20	1	0.14	2	0.14	2	85	3	85	3
1.2	–	18	2	0.14	2	0.14	2	110	4	110	4
2	–	14	3	0.21	3	0.21	·3	170	6	170	6
2.6	–	12	5	0.21	3	0.21	3	200	7	200	7
3.2	⅛	10	7	0.21	3	0.21	3	250	9	250	9
4	5/32	8	10	0.21	3	0.21	3	280	10	280	10
5	3/16	6	13	0.28	4	0.28	4	400	14	400	14

As the thickness of work increases, the flame will be required to supply more heat. This is made possible by increasing the nozzle size and the regulator gas pressures (in accordance with manufacturers' instructions).

If you should attempt to weld thick metal with a small nozzle by increasing the gas pressure, there comes a point where the flame leaves the end of the nozzle, indicating too high a pressure. This results in a very noisy flame. It is always much better to work with a 'soft' flame, which is obtained by using the correct nozzle size and pressure settings.

At the other extreme, if you are tempted to weld with a nozzle which is too large for the work, by reducing the supply of gas at the blowpipe valves, instead of changing to a smaller nozzle, then small explosions will occur at the nozzle. This is because the gas tends to build up around the nozzle in small bubbles as a direct result of inadequate pressure. These small explosions indicate that the gas pressure is too low.

Welding Thicker Material

As the plates get thicker, different edge preparations are employed. These different edge preparations are shown below. You will notice that as the plate gets more than 4 mm thick, it is recommended that another technique, the rightward technique, is used.

Although, these days, it is more usual to use one of the arc welding processes on materials above this thickness, the rightward method is handy to know. Some welding courses include this method and a brief description is given here.

Thickness of metal	Diameter of welding rod	Edge preparation	Technique
0.9–1.6 mm	1.5 mm		Leftward technique
Up to 3 mm	1.5 to 3.2 mm	0.8–3 mm gap	Leftward technique
3 to 4 mm	3.2 mm	80° 1.6–3 mm gap	
5 to 8 mm	3.2 mm	3–4 mm gap	Rightward technique
Up to 13 mm	6 mm	60° 3–4 mm gap	Rightward technique

Above 13 mm thickness, plate can be bevelled and welded from both sides.

The Rightward Technique of Gas Welding

Some advantages of this method on thicker plate are:

1. It is faster and uses less filler rod, so it is less expensive.
2. There is less expansion and therefore less contraction.
3. The flame remains over the deposited metal, giving an annealing action.
4. A better view of the molten pool is obtained, allowing for greater control of the welding operation.

Gas welding can be used for welding in the vertical and overhead positions. These notes cover the flat position only, as you will need to perfect this technique thoroughly before you can learn positional welding.

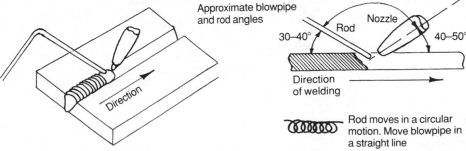

Approximate blowpipe and rod angles

100–110°

Nozzle

Rod

30–40°

40–50°

Direction of welding

Rod moves in a circular motion. Move blowpipe in a straight line

Direction

Test Your Knowledge

1. List the safety equipment you would require for gas welding.

2. What colour is an acetylene cylinder? What colour is an oxygen cylinder?

3. What type of threads are fitted to the acetylene supply?

4. What type of threads are fitted to the oxygen supply?

5. Draw a cross-sectional sketch of a high-pressure gas welding blowpipe and label the main parts.

6. What is the approximate temperature of an oxy-acetylene flame?

7. What is the liquid called inside an acetylene cylinder?

8. Why must oil *never* be used to lubricate gas welding equipment?

9. What is the correct method to check for a gas leak?

10. Sketch the three different types of gas welding flame and name them.

4 | OXY-FUEL GAS CUTTING

Equipment and Precautions

The basic precautions for this process are the same as those used for gas welding, however care must be taken to support work correctly, so that it will not collapse after being cut and cause injury. Because cutting is often used in demolition work and for cutting up scrap, particular attention must be paid to what scrap containers may have contained, or may still contain. This is of course to avoid the risk of explosion when cutting up drums and tanks and, for this reason, attention is again drawn to two publications of the Health and Safety Executive:

Booklet 32. Repair of Drums and Small Tanks: Explosion and Fire Risk
(This booklet also contains details of potential explosions from cutting operations on unsafe containers or in unsafe conditions.)

Booklet 50. Welding and Flame-cutting using Compressed Gases.
Both booklets are available from Her Majesty's Stationery Office and should be thoroughly studied by anyone intending to carry out gas welding or cutting operations.

Nozzles for gas cutting have either 6 or 8 holes, to give 6 or 8 neutral pre-heating flames, and one central hole for the high-pressure oxygen, which is released when the cutting oxygen lever on the blowpipe is depressed.

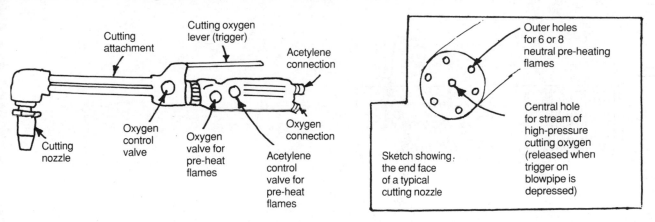

One type of cutting blowpipe which is made by fitting an approved cutting attachment on to the appropriate blowpipe shank

Gas cutting is often used to prepare the edges of thicker plates for welding, by cutting to the appropriate bevel.

Operations Involved in Cutting

There are two operations involved in oxy-fuel gas cutting:

1. Heating flames are directed on to the metal to be cut until it is raised to a bright red heat. This is called the ignition temperature – about 900°C.
2. A stream of high-pressure oxygen is directed on to the hot metal. This immediately oxidises the metal and, since the melting point of this oxide is below the melting point of steel, the oxide is melted and blown away.

The metal is therefore cut by a chemical action and the iron or steel is *not* melted. The heat needed to keep the cut going is provided partly by the heating jets and partly by the chemical action.

Blowpipes are usually of the injector type, so that they can be used on both high- and low-pressure systems. The modern type of cutting nozzle has the mixing chamber incorporated in it, so that a 'blowback' usually only goes as far as the nozzle, the high velocity of the gas tending to prevent it from going any further.

The size of the cutting blowpipe varies with the thickness of work, special heavy-duty blowpipes being available. Nozzle sizes also vary to cover different thicknesses of plate.

Cutting machines, where one or several cutting blowpipes can be employed, provide cuts with greater speed and accuracy than does hand cutting.

Because cutting is essentially an oxidising process, it must be made clear that little or no steel is melted, therefore the *kerf* (the width of cut) should be quite clean, and the top and bottom edges square. On examining melted oxides after cutting, it has been found that they contain up to 30 per cent unmelted steel – steel that has in fact been *scoured* from the sides of the cut (kerf), by the high-pressure oxygen stream. This scouring can be seen if the sides of the kerf are inspected, as *drag lines* will be faintly etched on the faces of the metal. An incorrect cut will show up these drag lines in a more pronounced fashion.

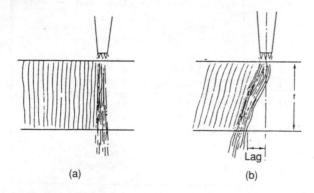

(a) (b)

Drag lines on cut plate: (a) vertical lines – zero drag; (b) drag measured against plate thickness – for example, 10 per cent drag means a lag of 10 per cent plate thickness

Examination of Flame Cut Edges

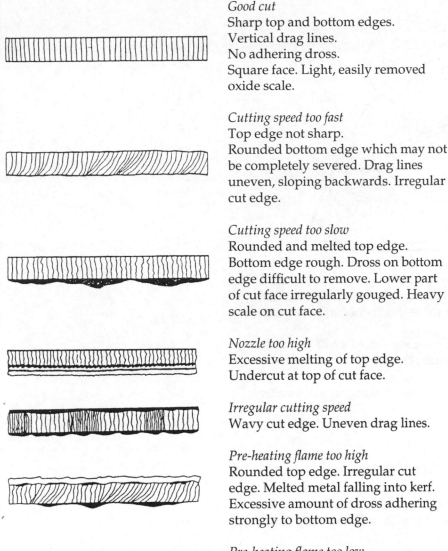

Good cut
Sharp top and bottom edges.
Vertical drag lines.
No adhering dross.
Square face. Light, easily removed
oxide scale.

Cutting speed too fast
Top edge not sharp.
Rounded bottom edge which may not
be completely severed. Drag lines
uneven, sloping backwards. Irregular
cut edge.

Cutting speed too slow
Rounded and melted top edge.
Bottom edge rough. Dross on bottom
edge difficult to remove. Lower part
of cut face irregularly gouged. Heavy
scale on cut face.

Nozzle too high
Excessive melting of top edge.
Undercut at top of cut face.

Irregular cutting speed
Wavy cut edge. Uneven drag lines.

Pre-heating flame too high
Rounded top edge. Irregular cut
edge. Melted metal falling into kerf.
Excessive amount of dross adhering
strongly to bottom edge.

Pre-heating flame too low
Bad gouging of lower part of cut face.
Cutting speed slow.

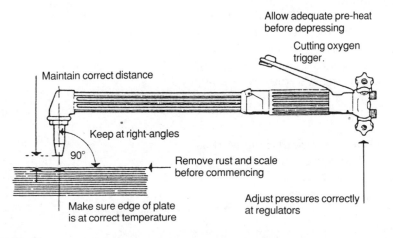

Tips for a good cut

Oxy-fuel Gas Cutting by Hand

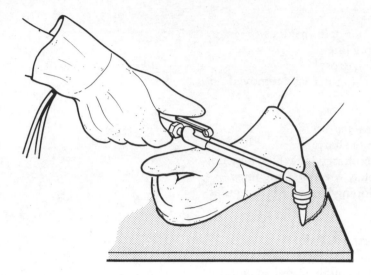

There is a fair amount of skill involved in maintaining a constant rate of travel over the work and therefore, the general quality of cut produced with a hand-held cutting torch is usually inferior to the quality of cut made with a correctly adjusted cutting machine.

Cutting guides can help keep the torch on the correct line of cut and a roller attachment can be employed to maintain the correct nozzle-to-work distance.

Hand cutting is often used for one-off jobs, when making repairs or alterations and for demolition work.

Oxy-fuel Gas Cutting by Machine

Modern cutting machines are capable of making high-quality cuts within close limits. Many machines prepare bevelled edges for welding without any additional dressing operation being required.

There are many different designs of cutting machine. Some machines have a single cutting torch, while others have many. One design moves the cutting torch or torches above the plate to be cut, while another design keeps the cutting head stationary and moves the work beneath it.

The simplest cutting machine is the straight line type, which consists of a carriage containing the cutting torch which is mounted on a track. The carriage is traversed over the work by a variable-speed electric motor.

Other machines, often called profiling machines, can guide the cutting head or heads by following a template. Some guiding systems have a magnetic wheel device which will follow the outline of a steel template, while others contain a photo-electric cell which will follow the black outline of a drawing.

With all these machines, care should be taken to ensure that the work is correctly supported so that it will not collapse after being cut, thus reducing the risk of injury to the operator or damage to the machine.

5 | ELECTRIC ARC WELDING

The Basic Principles of Arc Welding

In both gas welding and arc welding, the edges of the parts being joined are melted and, if necessary, further metal is added to help form a molten pool between the two parts. The molten pool is then allowed to cool to form the joint. The completed weld is therefore the result of a series of solidified molten pools. We can see this on most welds by looking at the weld ripples – each ripple is the edge of a solidified molten pool.

The obvious difference between the two methods is that with oxy-acetylene welding, the heat to obtain the molten pool is obtained from the chemical energy of burning acetylene in oxygen, whereas electricity is used for arc welding.

✱   **FOR INTEREST**

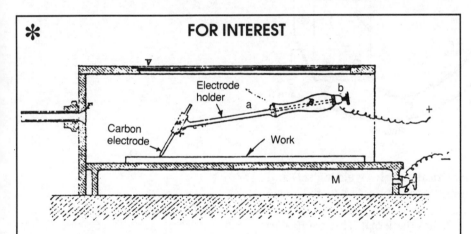

De Méritens' carbon arc welding machine as shown in the French patent of 1881

The diagram shows how arc welding was used to join the parts of a storage battery using a carbon electrode. A carbon electrode is classed as non-consumable, that is, it does not melt to form part of the weld. Modern-day TAGS welding uses a non-consumable tungsten electrode, so that extra metal has to be added in the form of a filler rod. Manual metal arc welding and MAGS welding use consumable electrodes which melt to form extra metal for the weld.

Manual Metal Arc Welding

In arc welding, then, electricity is used to form an electric arc. An example of an electric arc is the spark produced by the sparking plug on a car or motorcycle engine. The gap between the electrodes of the plug represents a break in the electrical circuit. Because the gap is small, an electric current of high enough voltage (or pressure) can force electricity to jump the air gap in the form of a large spark or arc.

An electric arc is therefore really the same as a spark, except that a spark only lasts for a split second, whereas an arc may continue for some time. An electric arc is formed when an electric current passes between two electrodes separated by a small air gap. In arc welding, one electrode is the welding rod or wire (called the electrode), while the other is the metal being welded. While the arc is operating, heat is released. Either direct current or alternating current can be used to establish an electric arc between the electrode and the workpiece. The voltage at the point of weld (before an arc is established) is known as the open circuit voltage.

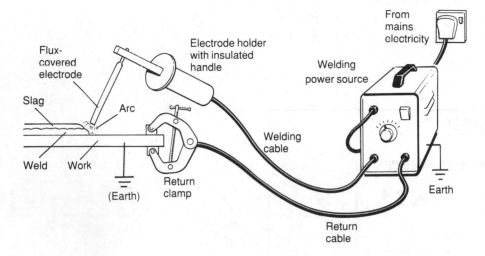

The work is connected to the source of electrical supply (welding set) and the electrode holder, held by the operator is also connected to the same source. The electric arc completes the circuit.

The arc will not start until the electrode touches the work. This completes the circuit. When the electrode is lifted away slightly, and a gap appears once more, electricity passes across the gap using the lined up atoms of (ionised) air as a conductor. The arc is stopped or broken by moving the electrode further away. Intense heat is developed (temperatures in manual metal arc welding measure up to 6,000°C). The heat at the upper end of the arc melts the consumable electrode while the heat at the lower end of the arc melts the parent metal (the metal being welded).

Check the safety notes in Chapter 2.

Starting Welding and Practice Welds

The first thing to remember, before striking an arc, is to check that the filter in your screen shield is not cracked. You can do this by looking at an electric light: it will appear very faint but should indicate if there are any cracks present.

If you are working in an area already designed for welding, it should have screening to protect other people from the rays of the arc, and the walls should be matt painted to avoid reflections.

As well as your shield, gloves and leather apron, you will require a chipping hammer and wire brush to remove the slag (burnt flux) from a completed manual metal arc weld. Always wear eye protection during this operation.

Chipping hammer and wire brush

Striking and Maintaining an Arc

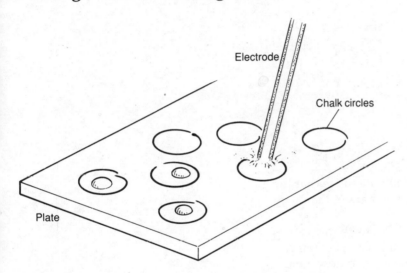

Practising striking an arc in the centre of chalk circles

TIP

One thing that usually happens when you are practising arc striking is that the electrode sticks to the work. If it will not free easily, then turn off the set. It will then come unstuck. As you get more experienced, this will very rarely happen.

There are two ways of establishing or 'striking' an arc. The first is to scratch the electrode across the surface of the plate (like a match) and then lift it slightly to form the arc gap. This method is obviously not very accurate and therefore not recommended. The second method, which is normally used, is to line up the electrode exactly over the spot where you want to strike, position your shield and tap down firmly. Once you tap down and contact is made, you must instantly raise the electrode to the required arc gap. For most smaller sizes of electrode, this arc length should be approximately the same as the diameter of the electrode. You must also get used to feeding down the electrode steadily as it burns away. One of the best methods of practising arc striking is to draw some chalk circles on a piece of scrap and then try and strike in the centre of each circle every time.

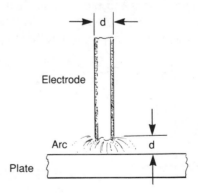

Arc length

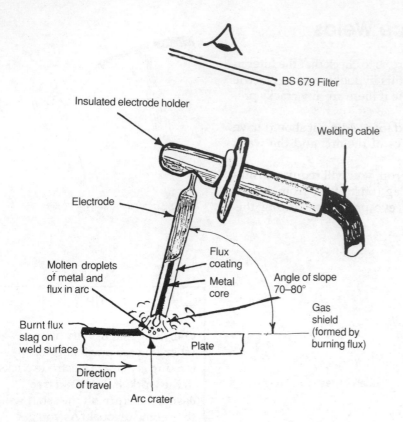

The manual metal arc process

As you practise with manual metal arc welding, you will notice that the heat is more concentrated and the welding speeds are much faster than with gas welding.

The coating on the welding electrode is flux, which burns to form a gas shield, protecting the molten weld metal from the atmosphere and helping to remove impurities. The flux also helps the metal to transfer and flow, finally setting in a hard 'slag' covering on the surface of the weld, and further protecting it as it cools down. This slag is later removed by the welder using the chipping hammer and wire brush. Clear goggles must be worn for this operation as slag is usually very hot and flies from the work in needle-like fragments during the chipping operation.

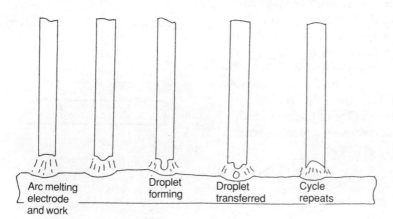

This sketch shows how droplets of molten metal are transferred from the end of the electrode to the molten pool of the weld

This table gives the typical welding current data for a mild steel electrode. Data on the packet should always be consulted as there can be variations with different makes of electrode.

Electrode size		Typical current in amps	Length of electrode (mm)
(mm)	(SWG)		
1.6	16	25	250
2.0	14	45	350
2.5	12	65	350
3.5	10	115	450
4.0	8	145	450
5.0	6	215	450
6.0	4	265	450
6.3	(¼ in.)	285	450
7.0	2	320	450
8.0	(⁵⁄₁₆ in.)	360	450

SWG stands for 'standard wire gauge'.

With experience, you will be able to adjust the setting given in the table slightly, one way or the other, as the type of work changes. The table is intended just as a guide to get you started.

Welding Straight Beads

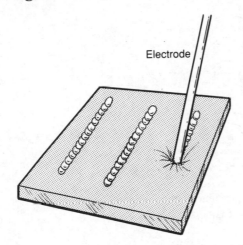

Electrode

When you have mastered striking the arc and maintaining it, the next stage is to practise straight runs or beads of weld. Again, try and use some scrap plate (make sure it is thick enough, so that you won't burn it through), draw some straight chalk lines on the plate and try welding along the lines to give a good, straight, even bead.

This is good practice in getting your rate of electrode feed right, so that the arc is kept at the correct length and also the speed of travel is such as to give the desired width of bead. The electrode should be held at 90° with a slope angle of 70° to 80° in the direction of travel. Chip and wire-brush every completed bead, and then give each a visual examination.

!	NOTE

Certain special electrodes, including stainless steel, are shorter than the values given to prevent overheating.

Restarting a Weld

Because electrodes will often run out in the middle of a weld, or before the weld is completed, it is best to learn the correct way of restarting a weld as soon as possible.

The recommended method is as follows:

1. Chip and clean out the slag from the weld crater and back for at least 12 mm. Wire-brush the whole area.
2. Restrike the arc about 6 mm in front of the crater, then move the arc back into the crater and continue welding. By striking the arc just ahead of the crater, any stray marks will be removed as the weld continues.

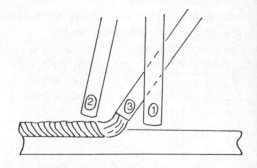

Electrode position 1 To strike the arc
Position 2 Moving electrode to the top of the crater
Position 3 Resuming forward travel

Defects can readily occur where a weld starts and finishes, so maintaining the correct procedure is important: gradually move the electrode round and slowly pull away at the end of a weld run, in order to prevent a crater at the end of a finished bead.

Most tests for welders include a section where the weld has to be stopped and then correctly restarted.

Weaving

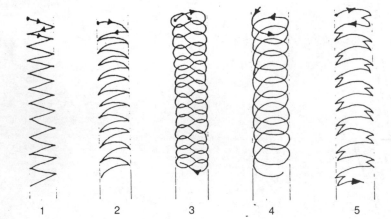

1   2   3   4   5

Sometimes a wide bead of weld is required. If this is the case, such a bead can be obtained by weaving the electrode from side to side, while at the same time moving the electrode forward to advance the weld.

There are a number of patterns. To practise weaving, deposit two straight runs of weld with a gap between them and fill in the gap with a weave. Try practising the different patterns shown above. The weave should be no wider than three times the diameter of the electrode.

Different welders prefer certain types of weave patterns. Type 2 is probably the most widely used, while the 'figure of 8' pattern shown in type 3 is preferred by other welders.

Some patterns are easier to do with certain types of electrodes. However, the beginner should practise weave patterns with all types of electrode, as the experience will be valuable in the future when different types of welded joints are attempted.

The Pad Weld

Sometimes a component can require a build-up of weld – as a repair or to deposit wear-resisting material.

As the pad weld is made by placing straight runs on top of each other, it is often used as a practice piece. Each run of weld must be thoroughly chipped off and wire-brushed, otherwise slag inclusions will form inside the pad which will weaken it.

The usual test carried out after visual inspection of the completed weld is to saw it through and give one surface a 'macro-etch' examination. An explanation of this method is given in the section on weld testing. Mechanised welding is sometimes used for large pad welds and the photograph below shows a layer of hard-surface material being deposited using flux cored wire (wire electrode with flux on the inside instead of the outside) so that it can be fed through the machine. Note the use of localised fume extraction.

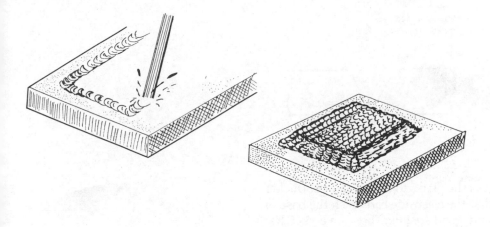

(Courtesy of TWI, Cambridge)

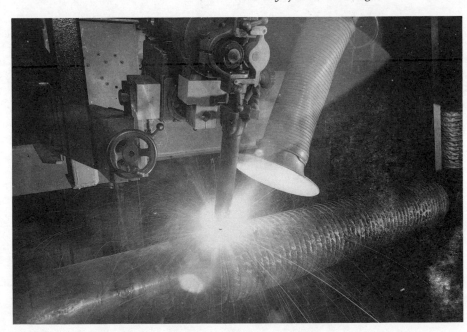

Plate Edge Preparations: Flat Position

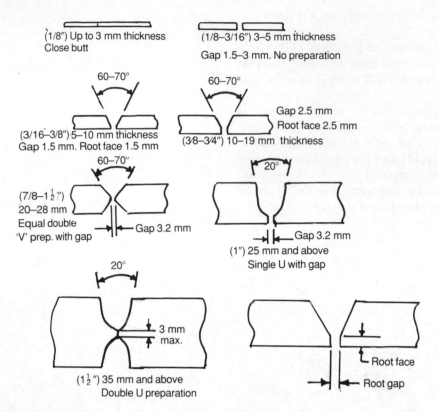

(1/8″) Up to 3 mm thickness
Close butt

(1/8–3/16″) 3–5 mm thickness
Gap 1.5–3 mm. No preparation

60–70°

(3/16–3/8″) 5–10 mm thickness
Gap 1.5 mm. Root face 1.5 mm

60–70°
Gap 2.5 mm
Root face 2.5 mm
(3/8–3/4″) 10–19 mm thickness

60–70°

(7/8–1½″)
20–28 mm
Equal double
'V' prep. with gap
Gap 3.2 mm

20°
Gap 3.2 mm
(1″) 25 mm and above
Single U with gap

20°
3 mm max.

(1½″) 35 mm and above
Double U preparation

Root face
Root gap

In arc welding, just as in gas welding, as the plates to be welded get thicker they will require preparing in order that the electrode can reach the base of the joint and give root penetration and good fusion. The above sketches show typical edge preparations for butt welds on different thicknesses in the flat position.

Manipulators

It is usually easier and faster to weld in the flat position whenever possible. *Manipulators* can be used to achieve this. These are mechanical devices that position the work.

Floor turntable manipulator: load capacity, 10,000 kg; table diameter, 1,525 mm; overall length, 2,000 mm; speed range, 0.1 to 2.0 r.p.m.; eccentricity, 300 mm; overall height, 550 mm; supply voltage, 240 V single phase; control – via remote pendant with forward, reverse, stop, speed and emergency stop (Courtesy: M.C.E. Co-Weld Ltd. Liverpool.)

An electric arc welder using a roller bed manipulator. (Courtesy of M.C.E. Co-Weld Ltd. Liverpool.)

The Two Main Types of Weld

There are two main types of weld:

Butt welds and Fillet welds

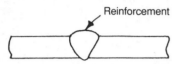

Single 'V' butt weld

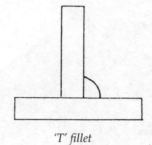

'T' fillet

All the variations of welds fit into one or the other of these two categories.

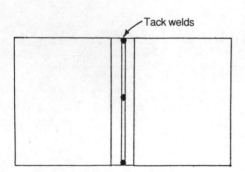

The lap weld is a fillet weld

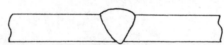

Butt weld edges are bevelled on thicker plates to allow the arc to reach the root of the joint

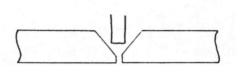

Weld showing correct penetration

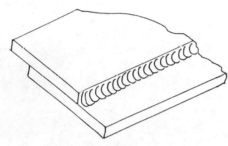

Tack welds

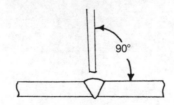

Tilt angle of electrode for butt welds – end view

Weld showing no penetration

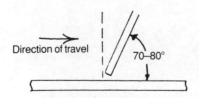

Slope angle of electrode for butt welds – side view

A slight weaving action can be used when depositing the final 'capping' run.

Techniques for Making Butt, Lap and Fillet Welds in the Flat Position

The welder should understand that any figures given for bevelling and spacing are suggestions for average work.

Exactness of preparation, the size of electrodes and their type, together with the skill of the welder, will influence all dimensions given. In most fabrication shops, such information will be given on the weld procedure and drawings.

Practice on Butt Welds

Butt welds over 6 mm thick usually require preparation by bevelling. The example used here is the welding of 10 mm thick plate.

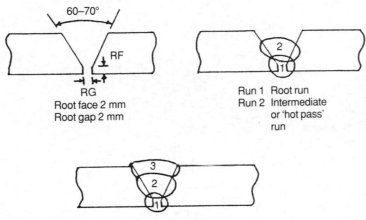

RG
Root face 2 mm
Root gap 2 mm

Run 1 Root run
Run 2 Intermediate or 'hot pass' run

Run 3 Capping run

1. The plates are prepared with a 60° or 70° bevel (see above note regarding exactness of preparation), and the required root face and gap setting.
2. The plates are then tacked together.
3. Run 1, the penetration bead, is then deposited.
4. After cleaning with a chipping hammer and a wire brush, deposit run 2.
5. Finally, again after cleaning, deposit the capping run with a slight 'weave'. Allow the finished weld to cool down slowly.

Fillet and Lap Welds

A fillet weld is a joint made by two surfaces that meet at right angles.

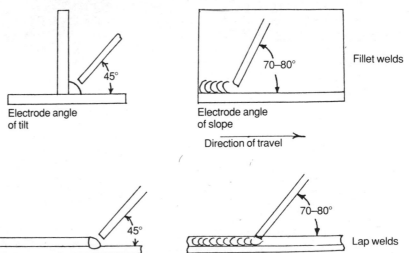

Electrode angle of tilt

Electrode angle of slope

Direction of travel

Fillet welds

Lap welds

The electrode slope and tilt angles are the same for fillet and lap welds

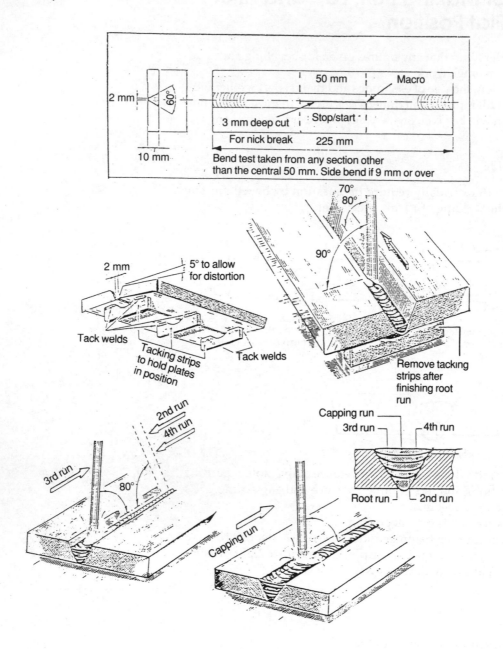

'T' Fillet Weld: Example Test Procedure

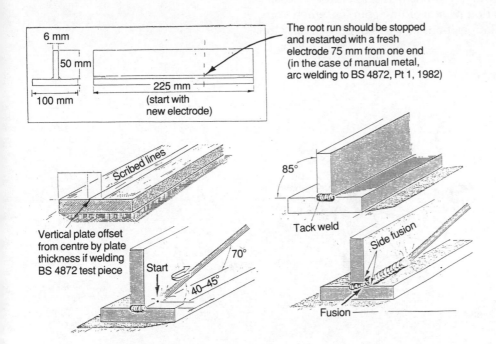

6 mm

50 mm

100 mm

225 mm

(start with new electrode)

The root run should be stopped and restarted with a fresh electrode 75 mm from one end (in the case of manual metal, arc welding to BS 4872, Pt 1, 1982)

Scribed lines

Vertical plate offset from centre by plate thickness if welding BS 4872 test piece

Start

70°

40–45°

85°

Tack weld

Side fusion

Fusion

Welding in Other Positions

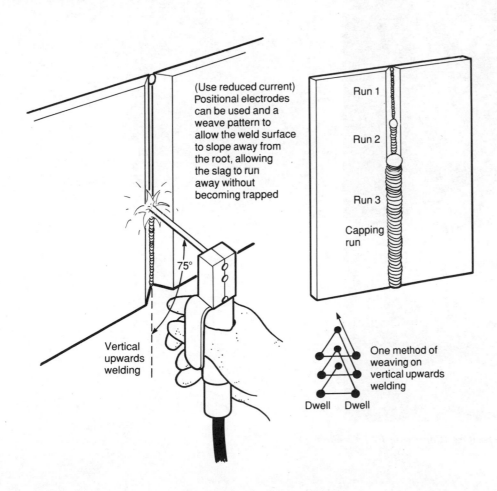

(Use reduced current) Positional electrodes can be used and a weave pattern to allow the weld surface to slope away from the root, allowing the slag to run away without becoming trapped

75°

Vertical upwards welding

Run 1

Run 2

Run 3

Capping run

One method of weaving on vertical upwards welding

Dwell   Dwell

As was mentioned earlier, it is usually easier and therefore faster to weld in the flat position. This is where a manipulator can help. It is not always possible to turn the work however, so that on most welding courses, when you have fully mastered welding in the flat position, you will be shown how to practise welding in other positions.

Horizontal/vertical

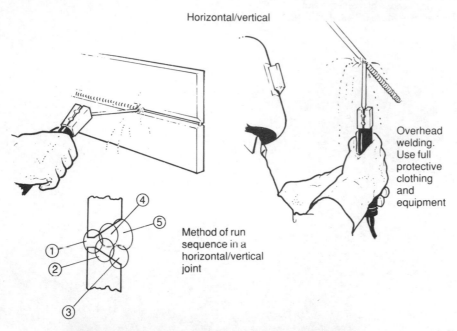

Overhead welding. Use full protective clothing and equipment

Method of run sequence in a horizontal/vertical joint

Manual metal arc welding in the overhead position. (Courtesy of TWI, Cambridge.)

Welding Power Sources

These are classified into two groups: alternating current (AC) or direct current (DC) according to the output current. (See also the sections on magnetism and electricity in Chapter 11 and three-phase AC in Chapter 8.)

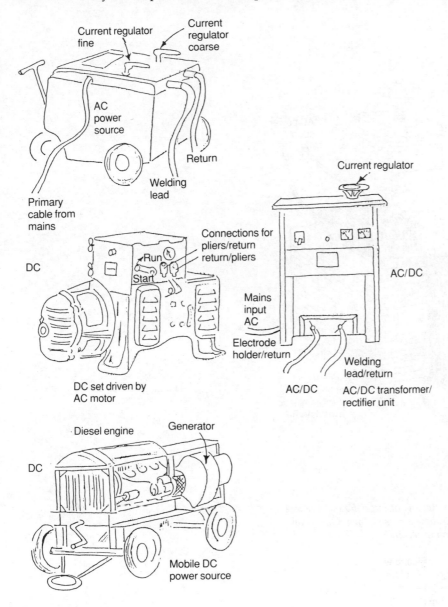

Generators may be driven by:

1. Motor connected to mains supply.
2. Petrol or diesel engine.

A rectifier receives AC from a transformer and changes it to DC.

AC Transformers

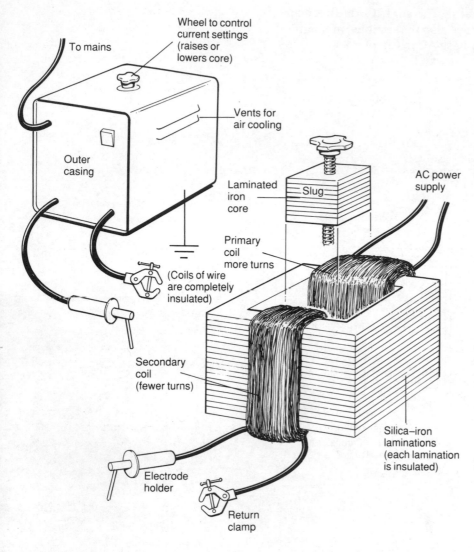

Wheel to control current settings (raises or lowers core)

To mains

Vents for air cooling

Outer casing

Laminated iron core

Slug

AC power supply

Primary coil more turns

(Coils of wire are completely insulated)

Secondary coil (fewer turns)

Silica–iron laminations (each lamination is insulated)

Electrode holder

Return clamp

This sketch shows a very basic AC welding transformer. Raising or lowering the core will raise or lower the welding current. There are many variations of this method. One simple variation is shown below – using tappings from the secondary coil.

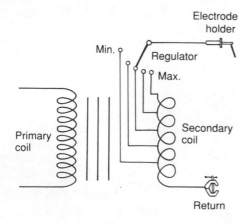

Electrode holder

Min.

Regulator

Max.

Primary coil

Secondary coil

Return

Striking the Arc

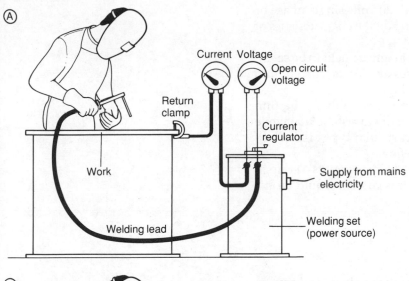

A

Current Voltage

Open circuit
voltage

Return
clamp

Current
regulator

Work

Supply from mains
electricity

Welding lead

Welding set
(power source)

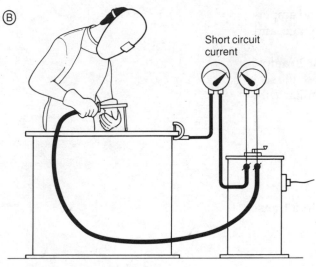

B

Short circuit
current

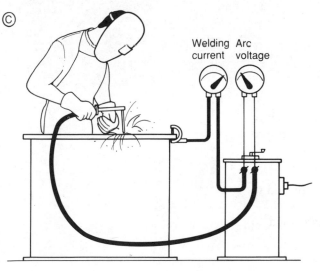

C

Welding Arc
current voltage

The voltage needed to strike an arc is between 65 and 85 V. In sketch A, no welding is being done and so no current is passing through the leads, and the ammeter is registering 0. There is, however, an open-circuit voltage present and the voltmeter indicates a voltage of 65 – 85 V. In B the electrode touches the work. At high current, the short-circuit current flows through the leads, the ammeter shows a large increase and the voltage drops to almost zero. The tip of the electrode and the point of contact become warm owing to resistance.

In C, the electrode is lifted from the work a short distance, and the air between the electrode tip and the work is made conductive (ionised). Welding current can then easily pass from electrode to work or vice versa. An arc is formed, and the voltage rises to 20–40 V which is known as the arc voltage. The current falls to the pre-set value of the welding machine, giving the conditions for normal welding. The tip of the electrode melts, together with a small area of the work (weld pool). Weld metal is transferred from the electrode to the work. A good welding machine must be capable of coping with variations in arc length.

Transformers

The power supply to the transformer can be either 220 volts single phase or 440 volts 3 phase. The amperage can vary depending on the characteristics of the machine, but is usually less than 60 amperes.

This supply is fed into the *primary coil*, causing a magnetic field to be set up in the iron laminations. The magnetic field induces an electric current into the secondary coil. This is the power used for welding.

Both coils are insulated and are *not* connected to each other. The thin silica–iron laminations are separated by either paper or varnish, so that while they can be magnetised by the primary coil, this particular type of iron will not retain its magnetism once the current ceases to flow.

Thin, separated laminations are used to keep the 'eddy currents' set up in them at a low level. If a solid iron core was used, this current would be at a high level and severe overheating would result.

Transformation

This is a method by which an AC power supply of given voltage and amperage components is converted into a supply with different voltage and amperage components.

Consider a power of 8.8 kW (8800 watts) made up of 440 volts at 20 amps. What is the amperage availability if the new voltage is 100 volts? (See the section on Magnetism and electricity in Chapter 11 if you are not familiar with Ohm's Law.)

Power (watts) $= V \times I$
$8800 = V \times I$
$8800 = 100 \times I$
Therefore $I = 88$ amps

You will note from the above calculation that the power input to a transformer must equal the power output from a transformer.

In an electrical circuit a transformer is usually shown as follows:

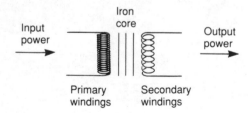

A single-phase transformer of the type commonly employed in welding (shown above), consists of a laminated iron core on which are wound two separate insulated coils, the primary and the secondary.

There are basically two types of transformers:

1. *Step down* – where high-voltage low-amperage current is transformed to low-voltage high-amperage current.
2. *Step up* – where low-voltage high-amperage current is transformed to high-voltage low-amperage current.

Transformation system (1) is employed on welding power sources.

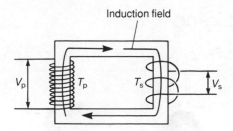

Induction field

Transformation is directly proportional to the number of turns of wire on both sides of the core.

If T_p = number of turns on primary side
and T_s = number of turns on secondary side

then $\dfrac{\text{EMF (electromotive force) induced in the secondary}}{\text{EMF (electromotive force) induced in the primary}} = \dfrac{T_s}{T_p}$

and $\dfrac{\text{Secondary Voltage } (V_s)}{\text{Primary Voltage } (V_p)} = \dfrac{T_s}{T_p}$

Example

In the circuit indicated above, the primary turns number 256. How many turns of conductors are required on the secondary side to produce 3,300 volts?

$\dfrac{V_s}{V_p} = \dfrac{T_s}{T_p}$, therefore $\dfrac{3300}{440} = \dfrac{T_s}{256}$

$T_s = \dfrac{256 \times 3300}{440} = 1920$ turns

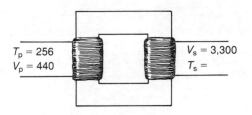

$T_p = 256$
$V_p = 440$

$V_s = 3,300$
$T_s =$

Comparison of AC and DC Welding Characteristics

DC equipment (generators or rectifiers) produces a strong directional flow of electric current from electrode to workpiece, or vice versa, depending on requirements.

The DC system produces extremely stable arc characteristics and is employed widely on pipe welding or positional work under difficult conditions where possible variations in arc length can occur.

An AC or alternating current produced by a transformer is less stable because of its alternating cycle. However, modern electrodes are designed to compensate for this characteristic by the addition of ionising agents.

With AC the open circuit or striking voltage is usually in the region of 80 volts. This reduces to 25 or 28 volts once the arc is established. ICI and some of the larger manufacturing companies include open circuit safety devices to reduce the effect of accidental electric shock.

Two-thirds of arc heat is at the positive end of an arc. This factor can be controlled when using DC, as either the work or the welding electrode can be connected to the positive terminal.

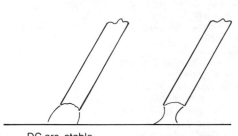

DC arc, stable and flowing in one direction

AC arc, changing direction with alternating cycle

Electrodes for Manual Metal Arc Welding

This section explains how to de-code the information on electrode packet labels. This current electrode classification is extracted from information given in British Standard 639 (1986). Students intending to continue studies in welding should consult the complete document, as it explains the various tests carried out.

E O O O O B [16 0 1 0 H]

The General Code is known as the STC Code as it covers strength, toughness and covering.
Any additional coding is in brackets following the STC Code

STC Code

'E' means a covered electrode for manual metal arc welding

Two digits indicating the tensile strength, yield strength and elongation properties of the weld metal (see Table 1)

Digit indicating temperatures for a minimum average impact value of 28 J (see Table 2)

Digit indicating temperatures for a minimum average impact value of 47 J (see Table 3)

Letter or letters indicating the type of covering as follows:
B – basic
BB – basic, high efficiency
C – cellulosic
R – rutile
RR – rutile, heavy coated
S – other types
Electrodes containing iron powder or other materials which would not affect the characteristics of the particular type of covering are classified by the letter or letters for the type of covering and not by the letter S (see 'Types of electrode flux coverings')

Bracket to indicate start of additional coding

The United Kingdom is participating in the work of international standardisation and any proposed changes to future standards would take this work into account

Bracket to indicate finish of additional coding

A letter H indicates that the electrode is hydrogen controlled. This means it will deposit not more than 15 ml of diffusible hydrogen per 100 grams of deposited weld metal. This reduces the danger of cold cracking

This digit indicates the recommended welding current and open circuit voltage conditions for the electrode. The various digits used to indicate different conditions are listed in Table 4

This digit indicates the recommended welding position(s) for using the electrode (BS499: Part 1 gives the definitions):
1 – All positions
2 – All positions except vertical/down
3 – Flat and, for fillet welds, horizontal/vertical
4 – Flat
5 – Flat, vertical/down and for fillet welds horizontal/vertical
9 – Any position or combination of positions not classified above

When appropriate, three digits indicating the nominal electrode efficiency, which is the ratio of the mass of weld metal deposited compared with the mass of core wire consumed for a given electrode. It is also known as the recovery rate and can be much greater than 100 per cent when iron powder is added to the flux coating. The efficiency figure is included in the classification only if it equals or exceeds 110

Types of Electrode Flux Coverings

Class C – cellulosic

These are manufactured from organic materials containing cellulose.

Characteristics: These coatings produce a large gas shield. They are noted for giving good penetration welds at high deposition rates and have an easily removable slag. They are often used for 'stovepipe' welding, that is, depositing the first run (or stringer bead) when pipe welding vertically downwards. The deposit can contain high levels of hydrogen. They are suitable for welding steel with AC or DC electrode positive.

Class B – basic

These fluxes are manufactured from calcium carbonate, calcium fluoride and other carbonates.

Characteristics: The heat of the arc decomposes the calcium carbonate, giving carbon dioxide which provides the gas shield. The calcium oxide and calcium fluoride combine to form a low melting point basic slag. These coatings help to produce a weld with a low hydrogen content. This makes them suitable for welding thick sections as there is a reduced danger of cold cracking. The lack of organic material in the flux allows the electrode to be baked before use, thus further reducing the possibility of hydrogen in the weld.

The gas shield is only relatively small however, and therefore a short arc should be maintained. The electrodes are suitable for use with AC or DC electrode positive. Always store these electrodes in warm dry conditions, and for best results bake before using.

Class BB – basic high efficiency

Characteristics: These electrodes are similar to the basic class but have an addition of metallic material, usually iron powder, which melts in the arc along with the core wire, and which can raise the efficiency (amount of metal deposited) to 130 per cent and more (as opposed to an electrode without these additions).

These electrodes are used in the flat or horizontal/vertical position as their high recovery rate makes them difficult to use in the vertical and overhead positions. They are suitable for use with either AC or DC, and are usually made positive.

Class R – rutile

These are mainly titanium dioxide (rutile) but can contain other hydrated minerals and/or organic cellulose.

Characteristics: They are very easy to use, giving a smooth finish with medium penetration. They are suitable for use with either AC or DC, the fluid slag and fast freezing weld metal making them ideal for positional work, although high levels of hydrogen in the weld deposit limit their use.

Class RR – rutile heavy coating

These are very similar to the rutile class, but again have additions of iron powder, raising the efficiency to 130 per cent or more.

Characteristics: They are similar to the rutile class, but increased rate of metal deposition tends to make them unsuitable for positional work. Efficiency is indicated by a three-figure digit at the start of the additional coding.

Class S – other types

This class includes electrodes that do not fall into any of the above classes. The range therefore covers flux coatings which are little used and also newly developed types.

> ⚠ **SAFETY**
>
> Packets of electrodes carry a manufacturer's health warning which gives advice about their safe use. This warning stresses the use of adequate ventilation.

Electrode Classification Tables from BS639 (1986)

Table 1. Designation for tensile properties

Electrode designation digit	Tensile strength	Minimum yield stress	Minimum elongation		
			When digit of table 2 is 0 or 1	When digit of table 2 is 2	When digit of table 2 is 3, 4 or 5
	N/mm²	N/mm²	%	%	%
E 43 – – –	430–550	330	20	22	24
E 51 – – –	510–650	360	18	18	20

Table 2. First digit for an impact value

Digit	Temperature for minimum average impact value of 28 J, using 4 mm diameter electrodes only
	°C
E – – 0 – –	Not specified
E – – 1 – –	+20
E – – 2 – –	0
E – – 3 – –	–20
E – – 4 – –	–30

Table 3. Second digit for an impact value

Digit	Temperature for minimum average impact value of 47 J using 4 mm diameter and largest diameter electrodes submitted for classification
	°C
E – – – 0 –	Not specified
E – – – 1 –	+20
E – – – 2 –	0
E – – – 3 –	–20
E – – – 4 –	–30
E – – – 5 –	–40
E – – – 6 –	–50
E – – – 7 –	–60
E – – – 8 –	–70

Table 4. Welding current and voltage conditions

Digit	Direct current	Alternating current
	Recommended electrode polarity	Minimum open circuit voltage
0	Polarity as recommended by manufacturer	Not suitable for use on AC
1	+ or –	50
2	–	50
3	+	50
4	+ or –	70
5	–	70
6	+	70
7	+ or –	80
8	–	80
9	+	80

Try de-coding these two electrode classifications to BS639 (1986), and then check your results with the next page.

Example 1

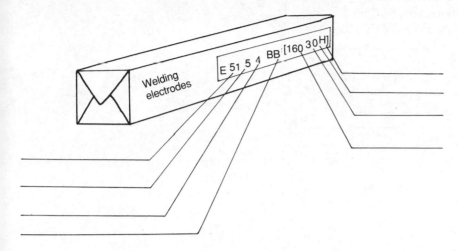

Example 2

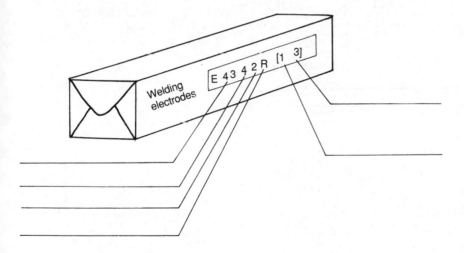

Example 1 of Electrode Classification

The classification of the electrode is

STC code   E51   5   4   BB
Strength (510 N/mm² to 650 N/mm²) ———————┘   │   │   │
Temperature for minimum average impact strength of 28 J (° C)┘   │   │
Temperature for minimum average impact strength of 47 J (°C) ————————┘   │
Covering (basic, high efficiency) ————————————————————————————————————┘

Additional code   [160   3   0   H]
Efficiency ——————————————————————————————————┘   │   │   │
Welding positions ——┘   │   │
Welding current and voltage conditions ————————————————————————————————┘   │
Hydrogen controlled ——┘

Complete classification
The complete classification is therefore E 51 5 4 BB [160 3 0 H]

Example 2 of Electrode Classification

The classification for the electrode is

STC code   E43   4   2   R
Strength (430 N/mm² to 550 N/mm²) ————————————┘   │   │   │
Temperature for minimum average impact
  strength of 28 J (–30 °C) ————————————————————————————————┘   │   │
Temperature for minimum average impact
  strength of 47 J (0°C) ——┘   │
Covering (rutile) ——┘

Additional code   [1   3]
Welding position ————————————————————————————————————┘   │
Welding current and voltage conditions ————————————————————————————————┘

Complete classification
The complete classification is therefore E 43 4 2 R [1 3]

Test Your Knowledge

1. Draw a sketch of a weld and label the following (a) reinforcement, (b) parent plate and (c) penetration.

2. Draw a sketch of a weld, showing and naming any four defects.

3. Sketch the electric arc welding process, naming the main components.

4. What is the approximate temperature of an electric arc?

5. What is an electric arc?

DIFFICULTIES AND DEFECTS IN WELDING

Possible Causes and Possible Corrections
(ARC and Gas Welding)

Difficulty/defect	Possible causes	Possible correction
Incomplete penetration	1. Joint design faulty. 2. Welding speed too rapid. 3. Insufficient welding current or nozzle size. 4. Too large an electrode/filler rod.	Check root gap, root face.
Poor appearance	1. Current too high or too low – flame too large or too small. 2. Incorrect use of electrode/blowpipe or filler rod. 3. Faulty electrode. Incorrect flame setting.	Check procedure and slope and tilt angles. Dry or change electrode. Re-adjust flame, clean nozzle.
Undercutting	1. Current too high/nozzle too large. 2. Incorrect manipulation. 3. Arc length too long. 4. Welding speed too rapid.	Check angles so that arc force is used to fill undercut.
Excessive spatter	1. Current too high. 2. Arc length too long. 3. Arc blow. 4. Faulty electrode.	See Arc blow.
Arc blow	Magnetic field created when welding with direct current.	Use AC machine. Re-arrange or split return clamp. Use copper back-up bar or magnet to oppose field. Change direction of welding. Change angle of electrode when deflection begins. Use small-gauge electrode and more runs.

Difficulty/defect	Possible causes	Possible correction
Pin holes	1. Contamination of joint. 2. Damp electrodes.	Remove paint, rust, scale etc. from work. Check electrodes for dampness.
Slag in weld	1. Joint design contains too narrow an included angle. 2. High viscosity of molten metal. 3. Rapid chilling. 4. Too low a weld temperature.	Use pre-heat. Failure to remove slag from previous weld in multi-run welds.
Porous welds	1. Weld speed too rapid. 2. Current too low. 3. High sulphur or other impurities in metal. 4. Faulty electrodes.	Use low hydrogen electrodes or process.
Cracked welds	1. Faulty electrodes. 2. Stressed welds. 3. Shape of weld bead incorrect. 4. Craters present. 5. Too fast a cooling rate.	1. Use low hydrogen electrodes. 2. Redesign work or jig, or pre-heat. 3. Use slower travel speed. 4. Fill craters. 5. Post-heat as well as pre-heat.
Distortion and warping	1. Incorrect design of weld. 2. Overheating. 3. Incorrect welding sequence.	Pre-set work. Use skip or backstep welding.
Brittle welds	1. Incorrect choice of electrode. 2. Incorrect heat treatment. 3. Air hardening deposit. 4. Base metal pick-up.	

Distortion and Stresses in Welding

(Information common to all processes)

When metal is subjected to a source of heat, it will increase in size because of the expansion taking place. However, if the heat is applied to one area only, the expansion can be local and therefore uneven.

The metal surrounding the heated area can remain comparatively cool and will tend to prevent expansion of the heated area. Therefore, if the yield point of the metal is reached, permanent deformation will occur. Hence on cooling, the metal will not return to its original form but will remain distorted.

The same effect can happen when cooling – the surrounding cooler metal can offer resistance, and contractional stresses can also add to the distortion.

The amount of distortion that takes place has a large influence on the amount of structural strain that will stay in the metal after it has cooled.

As the amount of distortion increases, the amount of strain in the metal will be reduced, influenced by a reduction in plastic flow. However, if restraint is placed on the metal to prevent distortion, residual stresses will remain after the metal has cooled and the final structure will be in a stressed condition. This situation can be remedied in most instances by a process known as *stress-relieving*, which involves controlled re-heating of the component to a carefully pre-determined temperature which is normally below the recrystallisation temperature, and therefore stress can be removed without too much disturbance of the metal's grain structure.

In welding, the amount of weld metal deposited, compared with the parent metal is relatively small. Therefore the greatest amount of heat is concentrated in this area. Also, as the strength of the weld metal will be greatly reduced at high temperatures, and since it is such a small mass when compared with the structure as a whole, the weld will be forced to take most of the plastic flow as the structure cools. If this plastic flow is greater than the metal's ultimate tensile strength, then a fracture can result.

Types of Distortion

There are three main types of distortion which can be set up in welded structures if care and preventative measures are not taken. These are angular distortion, longitudinal distortion and transverse distortion.

One method of overcoming angular distortion is to pre-set the plates to be welded. In other words, they are set in the opposite direction, so that when distortion takes place, the plates will pull into the required position. A test weld can be made and the amount of distortion measured with a protractor. The plates for the actual fabrication can then be pre-set to the required angle, thus compensating for angular distortion and minimising residual stresses.

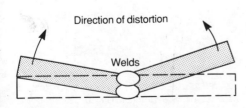

Angular distortion in a butt weld

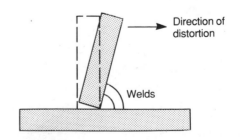

Angular distortion in a fillet weld

The fixing of electrical resistance elements for internal heating of vessel seam prior to welding. (Courtesy Cooperheat (UK) Ltd)

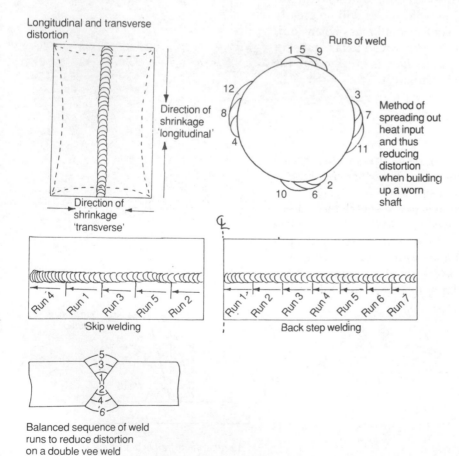

Longitudinal and transverse distortion

Direction of shrinkage 'longitudinal'

Direction of shrinkage 'transverse'

Runs of weld

Method of spreading out heat input and thus reducing distortion when building up a worn shaft

Skip welding

Back step welding

Balanced sequence of weld runs to reduce distortion on a double vee weld

As well as pre-setting of components, other methods of distortion control can be employed, based on ways of balancing the amount of heat being put into a fabrication during welding.

Distortion Control

Distortion can be minimised right from the design stage, by reducing the amount of welding to as low an amount possible. This can involve using folds in the material or using welding processes with the lowest heat input available.

If it was possible to pre-heat the component and control the cooling after welding, then distortion could also be controlled, but of course this is not always practicable.

There are ways of reducing distortion without pre-heating or pre-setting, using weld sequences such as skip and back-stepping and using the shrinkage of one weld to counteract the shrinkage of another, such as in the welding of a double vee joint or when building up a worn shaft.

It is important to remember that stresses can be introduced into materials during manufacturing processes, such as forming and cold rolling. Then, when the metal is heated during welding operations, the stresses are relieved but distortion is introduced.

Chills

A chill, when used in connection with welding, refers to a large block of metal placed adjacent to the line of weld. This acts to dissipate the welding heat during actual welding and to minimise the area affected by the welding heat input.

Heat travels by conduction, convection and radiation. Copper in the form of a block or strip is sometimes used as a chill because it is a very good conductor of heat and will therefore conduct heat away from the weld area.

Chills are therefore another method of distortion control.

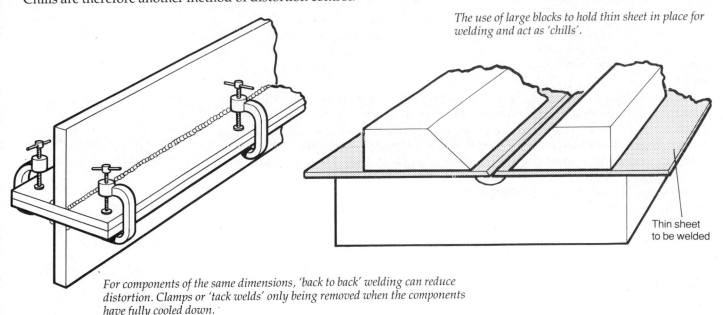

The use of large blocks to hold thin sheet in place for welding and act as 'chills'.

Thin sheet to be welded

For components of the same dimensions, 'back to back' welding can reduce distortion. Clamps or 'tack welds' only being removed when the components have fully cooled down.

7 EXAMINATION AND TESTING OF WELDS

Methods of Testing (Non-destructive)

The methods used in examining and testing welds are common for all welding processes. One of the biggest breakthroughs in this area has been the progress made in non-destructive testing (NDT). Powerful X-ray equipment or the use of radioactive isotopes enable us to look right inside a weld and examine the results on a film in much the same way as a surgeon would examine a medical X-ray.

Ultrasonic sound can also be used and, when the equipment is used by a skilled operator, it can produce information regarding the quality of a weld without the stringent safety precautions required for the use of X-rays and radioactive isotopes.

Miniature television cameras are often used to inspect the penetration of welds in small-diameter pipes.

Special dyes are employed in the 'dye penetrant' test. These dyes will find their way into any surface defects and highlight them on subsequent inspection, since after the work has been wiped, the dye will remain in the defect. Some dyes are fluorescent to ultra-violet light.

Magnetic particle inspection works in a similar way, when oil containing iron powder is spread over the weld area and the work magnetised. The particles will gather around any surface or near surface defect.

X-rays or radiographs are required when welding to certain standards, and welders have to submit their test welds to radiographic inspection and various destructive mechanical tests in order to gain higher levels of welder approval.

The Commmité Européen de la Normalisation (CEN) is working towards common welding standards for Europe. However, at present, students training to become welders in the United Kingdom usually work towards the standards given in BS4872, Part 1 (1982). All welds are first subjected to a visual examination under this standard before any destructive tests are carried out.

The existing British Standards BS4870 and BS4871 governing welding procedures and welder approval are to be replaced by European Standards BS EN287 (Parts 1 and 2) and BS EN288 (Parts 1 to 4).

Methods of Testing (Destructive)

The following is a list of destructive tests for approving welds and welders to BS4872 standards:

Test number and type	Destructive test(s) required
1. Butt weld in sheet	One macrosection to include the stop/start position.
2. Fillet weld in sheet	Three fracture tests after the end face at the stop/start position has been used for macro-examination.
*3. Butt weld in plate (without backing, welded from one side)	One bend test to be taken from a location showing full penetration other than the central 50 mm. One fracture test to include the stop/start position.
*4. Butt weld in plate (welded from both sides)	One bend test selected from other than the central 50 mm. One macrosection to include stop/start position.
*5. Butt weld in plate (with backing)	One bend test selected from other than the central 50 mm. One fracture test from the central 50 mm.
6. Fillet weld in plate	Three fracture tests after the end face at the stop/start position has been used for macro-examination.
7. Butt weld in pipe (without backing)	Two root bend tests taken from locations having full penetration, but for MIG welded pipe 10 mm thick and over two side bends.
8. Butt weld in pipe (with backing)	Two root bend tests, but for MIG welded pipe 10 mm thick and over two side bends.
9. Branch connection (fillet weld)	Four macrosections (one at each crotch and flank).

* In tests 3, 4 and 5, for plate less than 10 mm thick a root bend test shall be used; and for plate 10 mm thick and over a side bend test shall be used.

Cracking revealed by magnetic particle inspection. (Courtesy of TWI, Cambridge)

On site inspection of a node joint using ultrasonic equipment. (Courtesy of TWI, Cambridge)

Methods of Examination

The Visual Examination of Welds

Visual examination of welds is used to check for: size of weld, profile or weld face shape, any surface defects, undercut and overlap, any root defects and weld penetration.

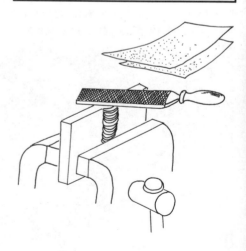

Macro-etch Examination

This is a destructive test, where level, polished sections of welds may be examined after etching, using up to 10 times magnification.

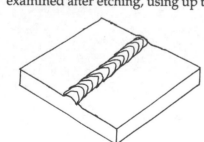

A specimen is cut out by sawing, and a small cross-sectional area prepared by filing or grinding the surface flat (using a coarse file). The coarse file marks are removed with a smooth file.

Using either emery paper laid on plate glass, or in the workshop wrapped round a file, polish with 'M', 'F', and 'O' grade papers.

Continue until all scratch marks are removed.

Alternate the direction of filing and polishing at right angles.

Immerse the polished surface in an etching solution of 10 per cent nitric acid in alcohol.

(10 per cent nitric acid in alcohol is used for low carbon steels.)

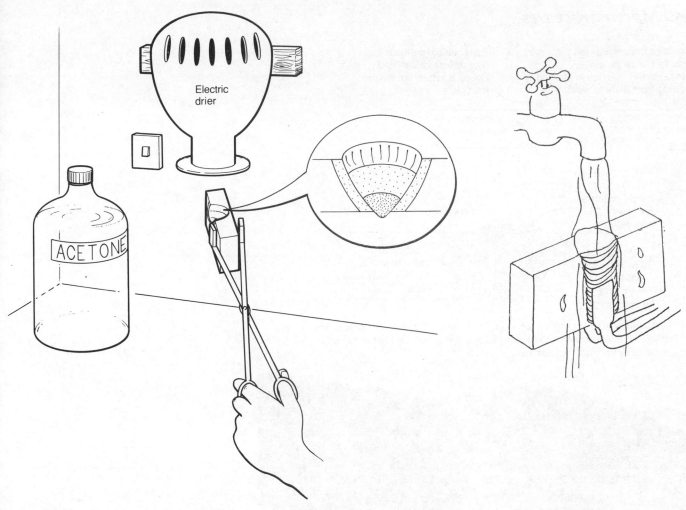

When a good definition of the weld structure has been obtained with the etching fluid, wash the specimen in hot water. After washing, rinse with acetone and dry using a hot air dryer.

An etched specimen can be preserved by painting it with a layer of clear varnish.

Weld Macrostructures

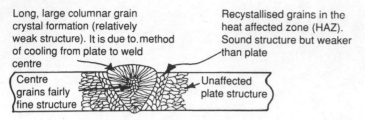

Long, large columnar grain crystal formation (relatively weak structure). It is due to method of cooling from plate to weld centre

Recystallised grains in the heat affected zone (HAZ). Sound structure but weaker than plate

Centre grains fairly fine structure

Unaffected plate structure

Typical structure of a single-run weld

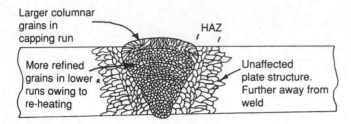

Larger columnar grains in capping run

HAZ

More refined grains in lower runs owing to re-heating

Unaffected plate structure. Further away from weld

Typical macrostructure of a multi-run weld. In the as-welded state this would tend to show grain refinement in consecutive weld runs, with larger columnar crystal formation remaining only in the final capping run.

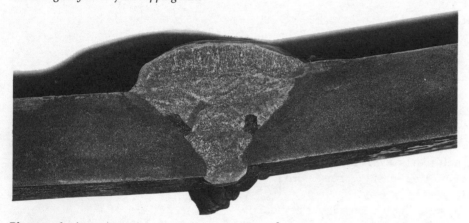

Photograph of a macro etch on a single vee manual metal arc weld. Note the two large slag inclusions and excessive penetration.

The Nick Break Fracture Test

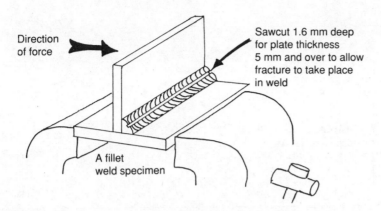

Direction of force

Sawcut 1.6 mm deep for plate thickness 5 mm and over to allow fracture to take place in weld

A fillet weld specimen

Breaking the weld open allows examination of internal defects. For this reason, the nick break test is often used during the training of welders. It shows the welder any faults in technique, and points the way to overcoming them. A good weld should fracture along the sawcut, leaving equal halves of the weld fused to their respective plates.

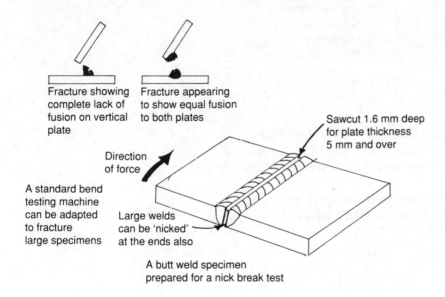

Fracture showing complete lack of fusion on vertical plate

Fracture appearing to show equal fusion to both plates

Sawcut 1.6 mm deep for plate thickness 5 mm and over

Direction of force

A standard bend testing machine can be adapted to fracture large specimens

Large welds can be 'nicked' at the ends also

A butt weld specimen prepared for a nick break test

Bend Test

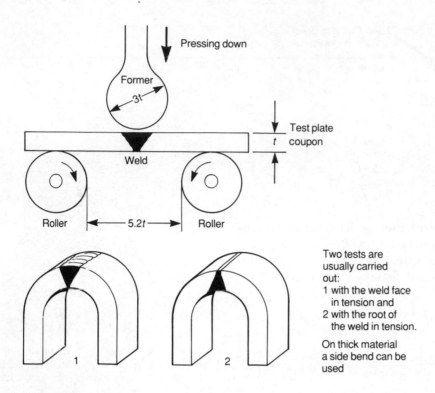

The principle of the bend test

The bend test, in one of the above forms is used to test the skill of the welder. If there is a fault in the weld, such as lack of fusion, slag inclusion, severe porosity or the like, the bend test will probably reveal it by failure of the specimen.

Specific sizes of specimen and formers are given, with each welding code requiring a bend test or tests, and these sizes should be strictly adhered to.

(See also the section on Tensile testing in Chapter 11.)

8 TUNGSTEN ARC GAS-SHIELDED WELDING (TAGS)

Basic Principles of Tungsten Arc Gas-Shielded Welding

TAGS welding uses an inert (non-reactive) gas shield, usually argon or helium to surround a non-consumable tungsten electrode, thus protecting the electrode and molten pool area from the atmosphere. This enables welding to be carried out without the need for a chemical flux.

The welding heat is created by an electric arc formed between the end of the tungsten electrode and the work. Tungsten is used as the electrode because it has a very high melting point (about 3,400 °C).

Safety Considerations

The precautions for protection of the skin from arc burn and the eyes from arc eye are the same as those for other arc welding processes, in that all skin surfaces should be adequately covered and shields or helmets should have filters to BS679 specification and of the correct shade.

The intensity of light radiation is greater with tungsten arc than with metal arc welding.

Precautions Regarding Electric Shock and Burns

All electrical equipment should be kept clean and free from dust.

Special care must be taken with equipment that is water cooled. If any leakage is noted, the equipment should be shut down immediately and the fault reported for repair.

As with other processes, all hoses and cables should be kept clear of hot or sharp metal and rough surfaces.

The welding current should always be switched off when either changing or making adjustments to the tungsten electrode.

Dangers from High Frequency

On most modern equipment, a high-frequency system is employed to start the arc without the need to touch the work. Care must therefore be taken, when the welding current is on, that the electrode does not come near exposed skin, as a high-frequency spark may be formed between the tungsten electrode and the skin surface, causing a severe burn and shock.

Care must also be taken to ensure that the filler rod is in contact with the parent metal.

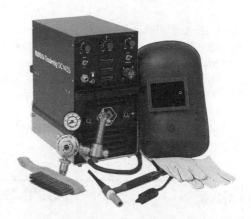

Small compact power source for use as a manual metal arc set or for TAGS welding. (Courtesy of Murex Welding Products Ltd)

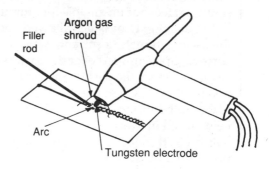

Extra metal is added by means of a filler rod as in oxy-acetylene welding. So that skills obtained in gas welding can be transferred to this process.

Generally, the amount of sparks and spatter is less with TAGS welding than with other arc welding processes and consequently, the protective clothing can be lighter. The gloves, for example, are usually made from lighter leather than those for manual metal arc and MAGS welding, giving better control and manipulation of the TAGS torch and filler wire.

Fumes

(See also Chapter 2)

As with all welding processes, good ventilation and fume extraction are required, but care must be taken not to disturb the protective argon gas shroud by too strong a draught.

With argon being heavier than air, it can accumulate at a low level in confined spaces, gradually reducing the oxygen level and increasing the risk of suffocation.

See also the dangers involved when working with degreasing agents (Chapter 2).

✱ FOR INTEREST

Welding of aluminium and magnesium had always been a problem with conventional manual metal arc and oxy-acetylene processes, as corrosive fluxes were required in order to remove the oxide film from the material surface and molten pool.

In order to try and overcome this problem, and atmospheric contamination during welding, inert gas was first employed as a shield in the early 1930s.

The first gas-shielded process employed a tungsten electrode and helium shielding gas and was called the tungsten inert gas (TIG) process. Direct current with electrode positive was used. With this system, the tungsten electrode tended to overheat and transfer fragments of tungsten to the weld unless a low current was utilised.

It was found that overheating could be avoided by making the tungsten electrode negative. This made the process suitable for welding stainless steel but unsuitable for aluminium and magnesium.

The development which allowed the welding of these materials was the use of alternating current, with a high-frequency, high-voltage current superimposed over the basic welding current to stabilise the arc. Using AC gives the perfect answer for welding aluminium and magnesium, as when the electrode is positive a cleaning action takes place on the surface of the weld and plate area, with particles of oxide being lifted up electrically, and so leaving an oxide-free area. On the next half-cycle, the electrode becomes negative, allowing it to cool slightly and preventing overheating. As the cycle repeats, the alternating current gives the perfect balance of oxide removal and electrode cooling, with the inert gas shield preventing further contamination until the molten pool has solidified.

Applications and Type of Equipment

TAGS welding is widely used in many industries, particularly aircraft, food processing, chemical, brewing and nuclear, where the advantages of not requiring a corrosive flux and the deposition of a high-purity weld can be used to full advantage. It is also used extensively for depositing root runs in pipework to coded standards in mild and alloy steels.

Because of these varied capabilities, the power sources are usually designed to provide both alternating and direct current supplies. In most cases, this means that they can also be used for manual metal arc welding.

This choice of AC or DC is made possible by combining a transformer and a rectifier, or a rectifier and an inverter into one unit.

The inverter type unit can change AC into DC by using very fast acting switches (called thyristors). These units are lighter in weight than the transformer/rectifier types but they are more expensive so the transformer/rectifier is the most commonly used type at present.

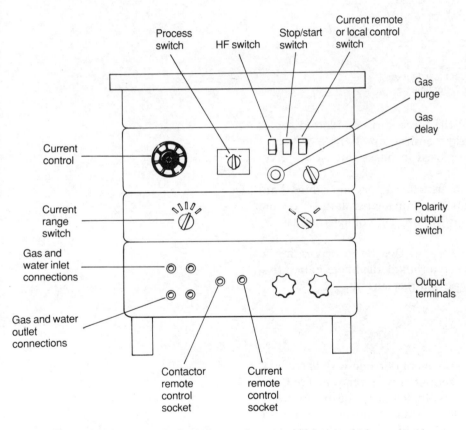

Sketch of a typical layout on a single phase transformer-rectifier unit which can provide either AC or DC output as required.

Electrical Considerations

Three-Phase AC

To understand the equipment used in TAGS welding, it is necessary to know a little about electricity. An introduction is given in this section, but also see Chapter 11.

One big advantage of alternating current is that more than one current at a time can be sent through the same conductor. Three different 50 Hz (cycles) currents can be combined in the same conductor. If there is a short space of time between them, they are said to be out-of-phase (see diagram).

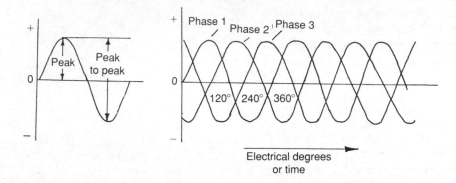

The diagram shows the three voltages of the three currents plotted separately. The overall effect can be measured by adding up all three AC voltages, or AC amps. If the three waves are placed in phase this would give large voltages and currents.

Three-phase AC can be handled with smaller conductors and cables than single-phase AC. This can give substantial economies when large currents and voltages are to be employed. Common welding set voltages are 240 V and 480 V.

An important feature about three-phase AC is that by incorporating a device known as a rectifier (sometimes called a choke), the lower half of the wave can be cut out, thus giving a wavy type of direct current.

Rectifiers

A rectifier can be classed as the electrical equivalent of a one-way valve in a high-pressure gas welding system, as the rectifier only lets the current flow one way. If the AC flowing into the rectifier is single phase, the output from the rectifier will be very wavy DC. If, however, three-phase AC is put into the rectifier, with all three phases separated (120° out-of-phase), then the DC out of the rectifier will be much smoother.

Types of Rectifier

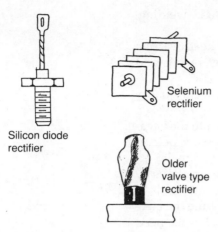

Silicon diode rectifier

Selenium rectifier

Older valve type rectifier

There are several different types of rectifier used in welding sets. One of the most common is the silicon-controlled rectifier (SCR). Silicon is known as a semiconductor material.

Before solid-state rectifiers such as SCR were used, vacuum tubes or valves were employed to convert AC into DC. Solid state means that the equipment does not use valves.

Selenium is another chemical element that is used in making rectifiers, as it is also a good semiconductor. The selenium rectifier looks like a row of cooling fins on a shaft. Each fin is one diode unit. Diode sections are added in series to increase a rectifier's voltage rating.

Mercury-pool rectifiers, which are like a large glass valve, use vaporised mercury to allow the current to flow in one direction only. These rectifiers are used in certain types of welding equipment where high power is needed. They are often used in resistance welding equipment.

The silicon diode looks rather like a big nut and bolt with a piece of braided copper at one end. Silicon rectifiers have a higher voltage rating than those made from selenium.

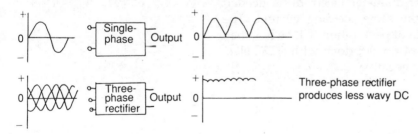

Alternating Current can be converted into wavy Direct Current by using a rectifier

Supply to the Arc

Both alternating and direct current supply is used in TAGS welding, depending on the type of material being welded.

DC is normally used for the TAGS welding of stainless and heat-resisting steels, mild and low alloy steels, copper, titanium and other metals and alloys that do not contain aluminium or magnesium.

AC can be used on steels, but generally will give inferior weld quality than DC.

With DC it is essential that the tungsten electrode is connected to the negative terminal, as two-thirds of the arc heat is generated at the positive pole. A tungsten electrode connected positive would quickly overheat and melt.

AC is necessary for the welding of aluminium and magnesium alloys by TAGS welding. This is because the surface oxide on these materials is removed automatically by the electrical action of the arc each time the electrode becomes positive, which is 50 times per second. This makes the need for chemical fluxes unnecessary. The alternating polarity with AC results in equal heat distribution at both poles. DC would be unsuitable, because, as stated above, if the tungsten electrode were connected positive it would rapidly overheat and if negative it would not remove the oxide film.

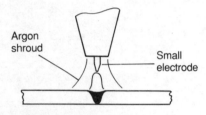

Deep penetration, narrow bead weld

Diagram of DC welding with electrode negative

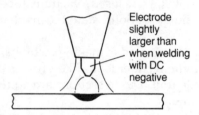

Medium penetration weld with medium width

Diagram of AC welding

DC Welding. When welding with DC most of the heat energy created will be at the positive end of the arc. Therefore, in order to prevent overheating and even melting of the tungsten electrode, it should be connected to the negative terminal of the welding set.

AC Welding. With AC welding, because of the polarity changes, a larger-diameter electrode is needed for the same welding current. The depth of penetration will be less than that of a weld done with a DC electrode negative.

Torches

There are many designs available, but they all fall into two main categories:

1. The lighter *air-cooled torches* made for the welding of thinner sheet sections. These are usually in three sizes: up to 50 amps capacity, 75 amps capacity or 100 amps capacity, but these ratings can vary with different makes.
2. *Water-cooled torches* are designed for the more heavy-duty welding for thicknesses up to approximately 12 mm, and can have current capacities from 100 to 500 amps. A fuse system is usually incorporated to cut off the current supply and to save damage to the equipment should there be a water supply failure.

Torches are air cooled for lower currents, up to about 150 amps and water cooled for higher currents.

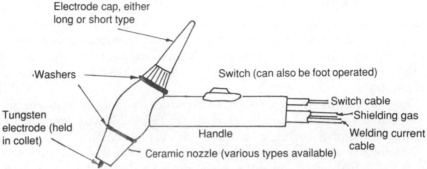

Sketch of typical air cooled torch

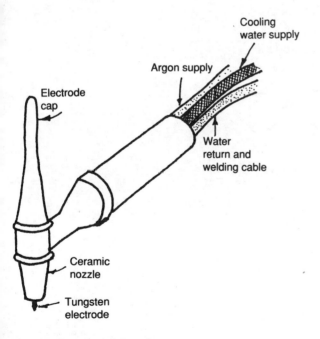

A typical water cooled torch

Hot wire tags welding – an automatic variation of the process. (Courtesy of TWI, Cambridge)

79

Crater-filling Device

A foot or hand control unit (on the torch) can be used for gradually reducing the current towards the end of a weld run in order to assist in filling up craters while still being protected by the argon gas shield.

Ceramic Nozzles

These are used with both the air- and water-cooled torches up to about 200 amps. However, above this amperage, metal nozzles with water cooling should be used.

Various shapes and sizes of nozzle are available to suit all ranges of work. These include shorter types for working in confined spaces, transparent types for improved visibility and extended types for welding in deep recesses.

The Gas Lens

Gas turbulance in the nozzle can sometimes result in poor shielding of the weld area. This can be improved by using a gas lens which will improve the gas concentration, allowing increased electrode projection (within the limits of the current-carrying capacity) if required, to gain access in difficult weld preparations.

The use of a gas lens can also help to reduce the amount of gas required when using a normal electrode extension/projection. The use also allows for greater variation in torch angles when welding positionally.

Gas nozzles are not particularly strong and the effect of constantly being heated and then cooled can make them brittle. They should therefore be handled with care in order to obtain maximum usage.

A 'gas lens' can be fitted to certain torches, between the torch and the nozzle. The metal gauze helps to increase shielding gas coverage and to allow welding to be carried out with greater extension of the tungsten electrode beyond the ceramic nozzle.

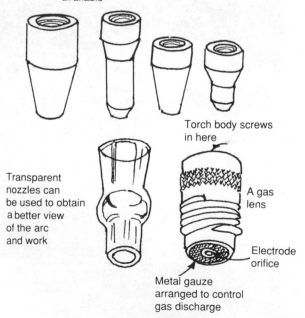

The standard nozzles are $\frac{1}{4}$" (6.5 mm) bore for air-cooled torches and $\frac{3}{8}$" (10 mm) bore for water-cooled torches. Large sizes and different shapes are available

Transparent nozzles can be used to obtain a better view of the arc and work

Torch body screws in here

A gas lens

Electrode orifice

Metal gauze arranged to control gas discharge

Tungsten Electrodes

In order to improve the quality of tungsten electrodes, certain additions can be made during manufacture. The main elements added are either zirconium or thorium. These elements help to reduce tungsten inclusions in the weld, increase the current-carrying capacity and the life of the electrode while also giving improved arc stability.

Electrodes with thorium additions – thoriated electrodes

These tungstens are used mainly for DC welding with electrode negative for stainless and heat-resisting steels, mild and low alloy steels, copper, nickel, titanium and others. They can be used with AC but this is not recommended for aluminium and its alloys.

Electrodes with zirconium additions – zirconiated electrodes

These have been specially designed for use on AC welding and are not as efficient on DC. Zirconium electrodes are especially suitable for the welding of aluminium, magnesium and their alloys.

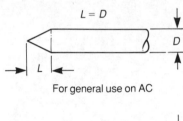

For general use on AC

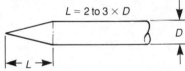

For DC below 20 amps

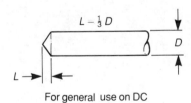

For general use on DC

Electrode preparation (approximate dimensions)

⚠	**SAFETY**

Always use localised dust extraction when grinding tungstens.

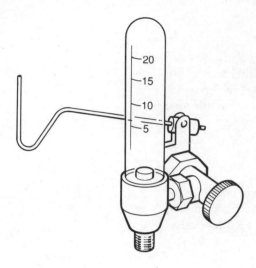

Flowmeter and gas economizer

Shielding Gas

Welding grade argon is supplied in steel cylinders painted light blue. The usual size of cylinder is 8.5 m³ charged at a pressure of 172 bar.

Care must be taken that the cylinder pressure does not fall too low, as the moisture level of the gas can rise as the cylinder pressure falls.

The flow of shielding gas can be controlled and measured by a valve and flowmeter.

A simple bobbin-type flowmeter is illustrated above. This type is also fitted with a gas economizer, similar to the type used in oxy-acetylene welding, with a lever on which the TAGS torch can be hung to stop the flow of shielding gas.

Some equipment contains automatic flow controls for both shielding gas and water cooling. They can operate in conjunction with the contactor and allow argon to flow for a pre-set duration before and after welding.

Initiating the Arc

During the initial development of TAGS welding, the simplest way of starting the arc used to be to touch the tungsten electrode to the workpiece. This caused the current to begin to flow. The electrode was then simply raised until the required arc length for the particular welding application was obtained.

This method was called touch or scratch starting and a carbon block was used instead of striking the arc directly on to the workpiece and risking electrode contamination. The carbon block could be placed near the start of the weld, the arc established on the block and then moved down the side of the block to the workpiece.

Touch or scratch starting was employed on simple TAGS welding set-ups using machines without special arc starting circuits.

A development that eliminates touch starting and avoids tungsten contamination is discussed next.

High-frequency Starting and the High-voltage Spark Gap Oscillator

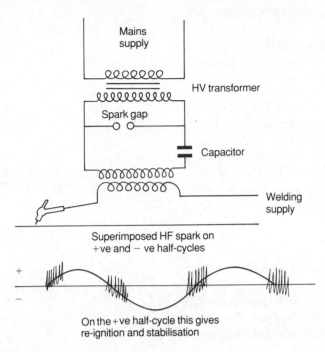

High-frequency starting and high-voltage gap oscillator

High-frequency (or HF) starting is a method of initiating the TAGS arc which overcomes the problems of touch starting. A high voltage (3,000 to 5,000 V) but very low-amperage (a couple of amps) current is combined with a high frequency (up to a million or more hertz and connected across the arc gap). The high voltage causes the gas in the arc gap to become ionised and allows a starting spark to be established. Such a device also helps arc re-ignition at the beginning of the positive half-cycle with alternating current.

The high-frequency spark oscillator consists of a transformer with a high-voltage secondary winding, a capacitor, a spark gap and another transformer which has one coil in the high-voltage circuit and the other in the welding circuit (see diagram). The capacitor is charged every half-cycle to 3,000 – 5,000 volts, and discharges across the spark gap in a series of spark oscillations. This discharge, on every half-cycle, sets up oscillatory currents in the circuit and these are induced and superimposed on the welding current through inductance in the second transformer. The discharge is timed to occur at the start of each half-cycle (although in order to aid re-ignition, it is needed only at the start of the positive half-cycle). The HF stabilisation with AC allows TAGS welding to be used for welding aluminium, as partial rectification can be reduced. Adequate suppression is required when using HF to avoid radio and TV interference.

Surge Injector Unit

The surge injector unit supplies a pulse surge of about 300 volts which is phased to come in at the exact point when the negative half-cycle changes to the positive half-cycle.

The surge injector does not produce a high-frequency spark oscillation, and therefore does not interfere noticeably with radio or TV transmissions.

Machines fitted with a surge injector usually consist of a rectifier unit supplying DC to a circuit containing resistance and capacitance. A surge valve supplies the short high-voltage pulses controlled by a trigger valve which releases the pulses into the welding circuit at exactly the right time, aiding the start of the positive half-cycle.

The surge injector is therefore an alternative method to the spark gap oscillator for maintaining the arc on the positive half-cycle. It will not usually be able to start the arc, however, so sets using this system have a high-voltage spark gap oscillator which is then taken out of circuit automatically once the arc is established.

Suppression of the DC Component in the AC Arc

Even with the use of HF, an imbalance still exists between the positive and negative half-cycles and there will be a DC component flowing. This can cause the transformer core to become 'saturated' magnetically and overheating to develop.

Banks of capacitors connected in series with the welding circuit will allow the AC through but block the DC component. They will also charge up on the negative half-cycle (because of the greater charge, resulting from the imbalance), and discharge on the positive half-cycle. In fact, at open-circuit voltages above 100 volts they will re-ignite the arc on each half-cycle, so that HF would be needed for starting only. The resulting increased voltage on the positive half-cycle improves the form of the AC waves, making each wave more equal. This equals out the heating effect between the electrode and the work, and the removal of the oxide film will be increased. Because of the cost of large banks of capacitors and the associated high voltages, most modern welding plant uses another method called *thyristor control* or *silicon-controlled rectification* (SCR). The sets using this method are fitted with the latest solid-state components to enable one control knob to be used. The welder sets the current control to the required value and a sensor in the outgoing welding supply checks this against the setting. The output of the SCR is thus constantly adjusted to that set by the welder.

Welding Technique

The Welding of Mild Steel

This section gives an example procedure for 1.5 mm thick plate.

Use a filler rod complying with British Standard 2901 A15. Set the argon flow to 5.6 litres/minute. Set the welding current in the range of 60–75 amps.

1. The torch should be held between the forefinger and thumb of the right hand. The handle of the torch should lie on the top of the hand and the hose assembly be supported by the forearm.
2. Lower the torch at an angle of about 70–80° until it is about 25 mm from the sheet surface at the right-hand end. With the welding current on, allow the argon to purge the hose of air and switch on the high-frequency start.
3. Position the welding shield and lower torch gently towards the sheet. As the tungsten gets close to the sheet, a train of high-frequency sparks will initiate the arc and the high frequency will cut out.
4. Lower the torch to maintain an arc length of about 1.5 mm.
5. Once the molten pool has been formed, the technique is very similar to gas welding. The filler rod is held in the left hand, between the fingers and thumb, and is fed into the molten pool at an angle of approximately 10–20°.
6. The end of the filler rod should always be kept within the argon shroud, making contact with the weld pool but not touching the electrode.
7. If the filler touches the electrode or the electrode touches the work it can be contaminated and will have to be re-ground to shape.

As with the gas welding, practice should be undertaken to produce neat straight beads of weld on scrap plate before attempting to joint two pieces of plate together.

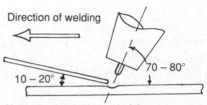

Direction of welding

70 – 80°

10 – 20°

Always maintain the end of the filler rod within the argon shroud, dipping into the weld pool but not touching the tungsten electrode

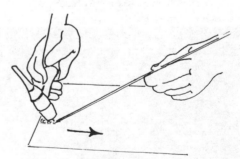

The torch should be held between the forefinger and thumb

Plasma Arc Welding (PAW) – A Variation of TAGS Welding

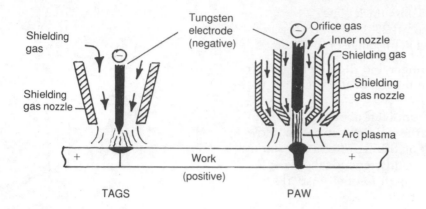

Plasma is ionised matter that carries an electric current. It makes up the arc of any arc welding process used in air or within a shielding gas.

As shown in the sketch, the only major difference between TAGS and PAW welding is that the PAW process has an inner nozzle into which is fed the gas to form the plasma and an outer nozzle for the shielding gas. So two gas cylinders are needed for PAW. There are two types of plasma torch: (1) the non-transferred arc, where the arc strikes between the tungsten and the nozzle and (2) the transferred arc (as shown in the sketch), where the arc is between the electrode and the work. Because PAW is hotter than TAGS, deeper penetration welds can be made with fewer passes and, because of the formation of a 'keyhole' right through the work, which is surrounded by molten metal which flows back into the gap, poor fit-up joints can be welded more easily.

Close-up of keyhole plasma welding. (Courtesy of TWI, Cambridge)

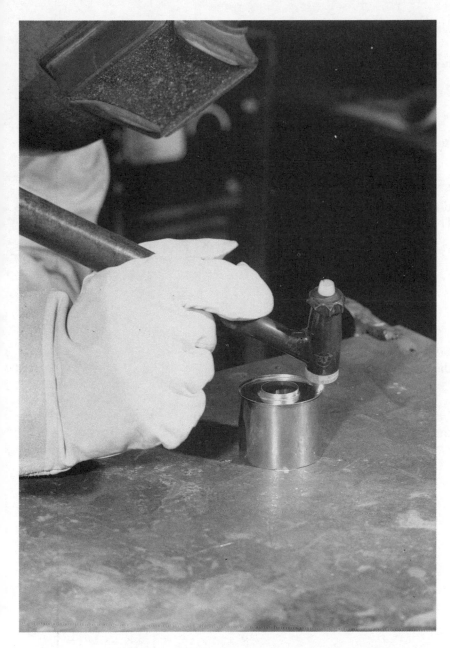

Microplasma welding. Plasma welding is a variation of TAGS, using a modified nozzle which heats the plasma gas sufficiently to conduct an electric current. (Plasma is a state of gas which has been thermally ionised) (Courtesy of TWI, Cambridge)

Test Your Knowledge

1. Why is alternating current necessary when TAGS-welding aluminium and its alloys?

2. What is the purpose of an HF unit when used for TAGS welding?

3. Give an application when (a) a thoriated tungsten electrode would be used and (b) a zirconiated tungsten would be used.

4. What is the purpose of a gas lens?

5. Why are the recommended filters to BS679 darker in shade than those used for manual metal arc welding using the same amperages?

6. What piece of electrical equipment prevents a DC component occurring when welding with an AC supply?

9 METAL ARC GAS-SHIELDED WELDING (MAGS) – SEMI-AUTOMATIC WELDING

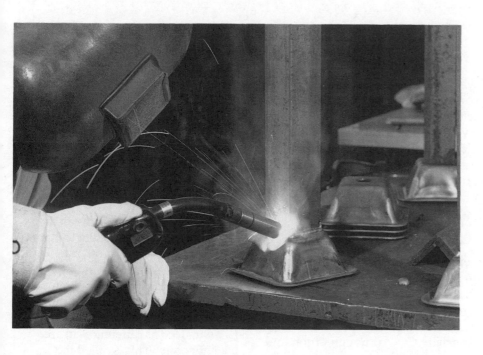

A MAGS (metal arc gas shielded) welder at work on a mild steel fabrication. (Courtesy of TWI, Cambridge)

Basic Principles of Metal Arc Gas-Shielded Welding

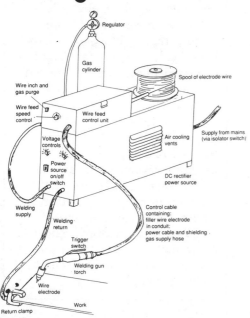

Regulator

Gas cylinder

Spool of electrode wire

Wire inch and gas purge

Wire feed speed control

Wire feed control unit

Voltage controls

Supply from mains (via isolator switch)

Air cooling vents

Power source on/off switch

DC rectifier power source

Welding supply

Welding return

Control cable containing: filler wire electrode in conduit; power cable and shielding gas supply hose

Trigger switch

Welding gun torch

Wire electrode

Work

Return clamp

Basic set-up for metal arc gas shielded welding

MAGS welding is a direct development of TAGS, replacing the non-consumable tungsten electrode with a consumable metal wire electrode.

Description

MAGS welding uses a direct current power source and a relatively thin wire electrode forming an arc to the workpiece. (A flux-cored wire can be used.)

The wire electrode is fed automatically from a spool, through a torch, which is connected to the positive terminal and is moved by hand.

The arc is self-adjusting, which means that any variation in the arc length made by the welder produces a change in the burn-off rate of the electrode, and the arc rapidly returns to its original length.

Applications

The process was developed from TAGS welding, with the tungsten electrode being replaced by the continuously fed consumable wire, and was first used only on aluminium with argon as the shielding gas.

When the use of carbon dioxide was developed as a cheaper shielding gas, the process began to be used for the welding of steels. The MAGS process (using a variety of gas mixtures) can be employed on steels of all thicknesses, aluminium, copper and many alloys, including stainless steel.

Safety Precautions

The general safety notes applicable to other arc welding processes are applicable to MAGS welding. Special attention should, however, be given to the section on fumes (in Chapter 2) as good ventilation is essential with gas-shielded processes. It is important to note that, in some instances, normal overhead type fume extractors may not work effectively when shielding gases heavier than air are employed (especially CO_2, although argon and other gases have been known to build up to dangerous levels when special care was not taken).

MAGS welding a T-fillet test piece. (Courtesy of TWI, Cambridge)

✳ FOR INTEREST

In MAGS welding, the electrode melts and molten particles are detached and transported across the arc to the work.

Unlike TAGS welding, the MAGS process is usually used with a direct current power source and the electrode positive. This gives fast melting of the relatively small-diameter electrode which can then be fed at a speed sufficient to compensate for this 'burn-off' rate.

With an automatic welding head, arc-length control can be obtained by a system which automatically speeds up or slows down the rate of wire feed as differences in arc length occur. This is called the controlled arc system.

In most semi-automatic machines, a system known as the 'self-adjusting arc' is employed. In this system, the wire electrode is fed at the pre-set constant rate through the flexible conduit to the hand-held torch. If the arc length is increased, the voltage is increased with a corresponding decrease in current, which causes a decrease in electrode burn-off rate and the arc length to be restored. Likewise, if the arc length is reduced, the process is reversible and an increase in burn-off rate occurs, again restoring the required arc length. This system, therefore, easily compensates for variations in electrode-to-work distances (arc length), which occur in a hand-held welding torch.

Equipment and Electrical Considerations

These semi-automatic and automatic processes have found increasing use in recent years and in some cases have replaced the use of oxy-acetylene and manual metal arc processes on certain types of fabrication.

The process is known by different names such as MIG (metallic inert gas), CO_2 welding (when a carbon dioxide gas shield is employed), metal active gas welding and in the USA, gas metal-arc welding.

In the UK, the most widely accepted name is MAGS – metal arc gas-shielded welding.

The process, being semi-automatic, has lent itself to full automation with certain types of work, and is used to quite a large extent in robot form.

The Process

A continuous consumable wire electrode is fed through a welding gun fitted with a concentric gas nozzle. The arc is struck between the workpiece and the wire, which acts as both electrode and filler. The arc and the weld pool are shielded from atmospheric contamination by passing a suitable gas through the nozzle to form a protective 'umbrella' around the welding area.

In the case of non-ferrous metals, pure argon is usually selected as the gas shield, although other gases, such as helium, or in the case of copper, sometimes nitrogen, can be used. For ferrous metals, carbon dioxide, argon and oxygen, argon and CO_2 and others are used.

Power Source

Rectifiers or generators providing direct current are essentially used with the MAGS system, with the electrode usually connected positive.

Wire Drive

The continuous electrode wire is driven by feed rolls, which are controlled by a variable-speed mechanism, housed in a control unit. This unit also contains automatic devices for initiating and stopping the flow of shielding gas, cooling water (with some systems) and the wire feed drive motor. Additionally, the unit contains the components for actuating the contactor in the power source, thus applying the welding current and voltage to the electrode.

When the drive rolls are incorporated into the control unit, the wire is fed through a flexible conduit into the welding gun, and on through the contact tube. For relatively soft or fine wires, the drive rolls and wire feed motor are located next to the gun for automatic welding heads, or in the handle, as in the case of the pistol-type air-cooled hand gun. The latter is also provided with a mounting spindle which will accommodate a small reel of wire weighing from 450 grams to 650 grams, depending on the type of electrode (that is, whether it is made of aluminium, steel etc.).

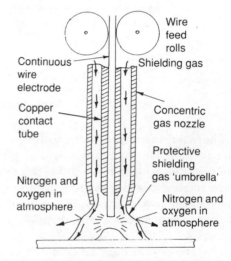

Schematic diagram of welding nozzle and gas shield

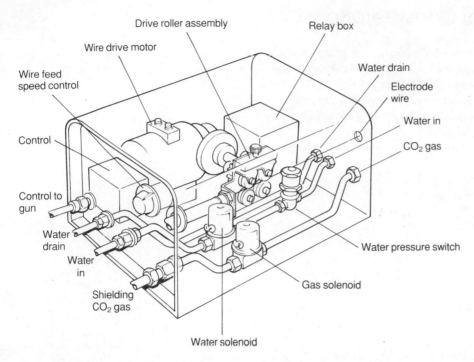

Drive roller assembly

Wire drive motor

Relay box

Wire feed
speed control

Water drain

Electrode
wire

Water in

Control

CO_2 gas

Control to
gun

Water
drain

Water
in

Water pressure switch

Shielding
CO_2 gas

Gas solenoid

Water solenoid

There are many types of equipment available both for industry and the
DIY welder. The feed rate is usually given in inches or mm per minute, and
the general range is from 50 to 100 inches (127 to 254 cm) per minute. The
wire feed speed on modern sets is usually controlled electronically. A
mechanical governor can also be used, or a constant-speed motor through a
variable speed gearbox. Another design uses a valve-controlled air supply to
increase or reduce the speed of a small turbine. Drive roll systems can consist
of one grooved roll (to suit the size of the wire) and one plain roll or both
rolls can be grooved. For smaller-diameter wires, drives with only one roll
being driven may suffice, while larger diameter and flux cored wires may
require both rolls to be driven in order to give a smooth and positive wire
feed. It is very important to ensure that rolls are in good condition and that
the pressure is set correctly. Too much pressure can deform the wire and
cause it to jam in the contact tube at the gun nozzle as this tube has only a
small clearance in its bore, to enable effective current pick-up. Insufficient
roll pressure can allow the wire to slip, resulting in an irregular wire speed.
Some larger wire drive units employ two straightening rolls just in front of
the wire feed rolls. This is sometimes necessary with large or very hard wires
which could leave the contact tube off-centre, resulting in lack of fusion or
lack of penetration at one side of the weld. It is important that the electrode
wire should not stick out too far from the contact tube when the arc has been
broken at the end of a weld, so an electronic control is therefore required
which is rapid enough to stop the drive motor, arresting the wire at the correct length of stick-out. Wire is fed from the drive rolls to the contact tube
through a flexible Bowden cable. Nylon and plastic liners can also be used to
provide a smooth feed for the smaller sizes of wire. Finer wires should be
carefully supported, as a kink in the feeding cable can lead to extensive
snarling of the wire. The feeding tubes should be regularly cleaned in order
to prevent a build-up of metal dust and possible wire feed problems.

Typical Wire Feed System for Metal Arc Gas-Shielded Welding

Wire feeds may be either a push or pull type, or a combination of both.

In the push type, two or more feed rolls are used and the pressure adjusted by a tensioning screw.

This method is generally used for feeding bare soft wire above a diameter of 1.2 mm and hard wire of not less than 0.6 mm. For flux-cored wires, the combination type is usually employed.

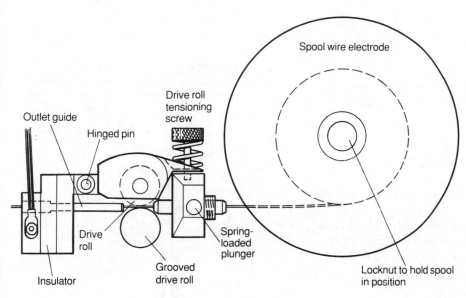

Wire drive unit - push type

Guns and Torches

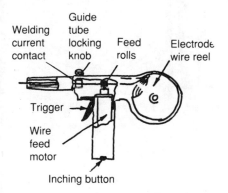

Reel-on-gun arrangement (pull type)

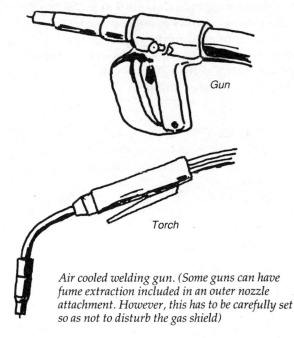

Air cooled welding gun. (Some guns can have fume extraction included in an outer nozzle attachment. However, this has to be carefully set so as not to disturb the gas shield)

Air-cooled Welding Torch

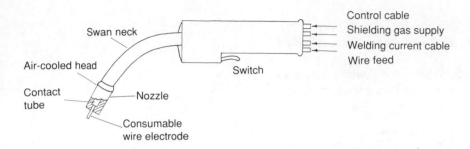

Shielding Gas, Cylinder Types and Contents

Carbon Dioxide

One of the shielding gases which can be used for the welding of steel is carbon dioxide (CO_2).

Carbon dioxide is suitable for use for dip transfer MAGS welding techniques.

There are two types of cylinder in use. The first type allows gas, which might contain moisture, to be given out on opening the cylinder valve. The second type is called a syphon cylinder (as shown in the sketch) and it allows only liquid carbon dioxide to be ejected on opening the cylinder valve.

Syphon type cylinders in which the liquid is drawn from the bottom of the cylinder should be used.

In order to prevent the regulator from freezing when the liquid CO_2 expands into gas, it is necessary to fit an electric heater/vaporiser unit between the cylinder valve outlet and the regulator when using syphon type cylinders.

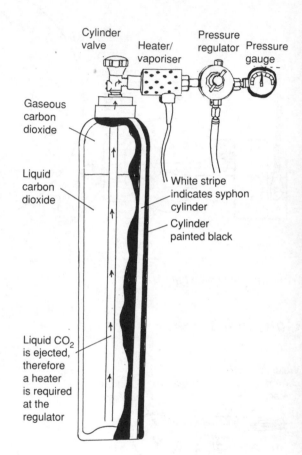

Some Other Shielding Gases

1. *Argon* – inert gas – cylinder colour *blue*.
2. *Helium* – inert gas – cylinder colour *brown*.
3. *Argon/oxygen mixture* – *blue with black band* (percentage of oxygen indicated) About 1–2 per cent of oxygen is added when welding stainless steels and 2–5 per cent when welding mild steel by spray transfer. For pulse transfer, argon mixed with up to 2 per cent oxygen and up to 5 per cent of carbon dioxide can be used for welding steels.
4. *Argon/carbon dioxide mixtures* – cylinder colour *blue and green band* (percentage mixture indicated). Dip and spray transfer techniques are possible with mixed shielding gas of argon and from 5 to 25 per cent of carbon dioxide.

Metal Transfer in MAGS Welding

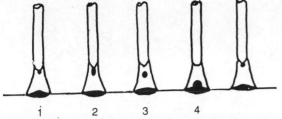

1. Droplet forming.
2. Droplet being 'pinched' off.
3. Droplet in free flight.
4. Droplet deposited in molten pool.

Spray transfer

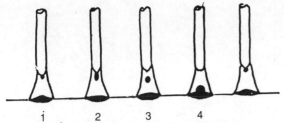

1. Electrode short-circuits.
2. Current increases.
3. Arc re-ignited.
4. End of electrode heating up.
5. Electrode about to short-circuit. Cycle repeats.

Dip or short circuiting transfer

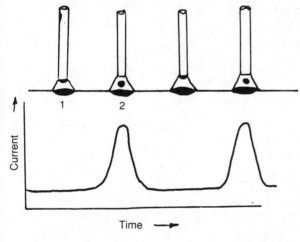

1. Background current maintaining arc.
2. Pulsed current projects metal droplet across the arc gap.

Pulsed arc transfer

Spray transfer can be divided into two different modes. The true spray is obtained when the shielding gas is argon or argon/oxygen mixture. With these gas shields, the droplets in the spray are very fine and never short-circuit the arc. When carbon dioxide or argon/carbon dioxide mixture is used, a molten ball tends to form at the end of the electrode and can grow in size until its diameter is greater than the electrode diameter. These large droplets can cause short circuits to occur and this mode is known as 'globular transfer'. With conditions that cause the short circuits to occur very rapidly, the mode becomes 'short-circuiting' or 'dip' transfer.

There are three main types of metal transfer with MAGS welding, although one of them, pulsed transfer, is a type of spray transfer.

It will be seen from the graph above that smaller welding power sources below 200 amps will not be able to operate in the spray transfer range and so are usually confined to the dip transfer mode.

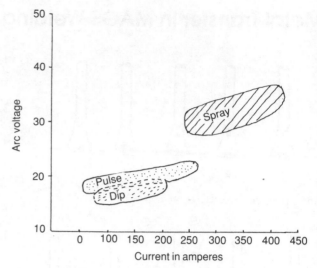

Approximate voltage and current ranges for dip, pulsed and spray transfer using 1.25 mm wire

Spray Transfer

In spray transfer, droplets of metal are transferred from the end of the electrode in the form of a fine spray. It is usually used for the welding of thicker plate in the flat and horizontal/vertical positions.

As spray transfer requires the use of higher welding currents and arc voltages, the resulting fluid state of the molten pool does not allow it to be used for the welding of steels in positions other than flat or horizontal/vertical. Aluminium, however, can be welded in all positions using spray transfer.

Pulsed Transfer

Pulsed transfer enables the droplets of metal to be controlled by the use of a regular frequency of pulses supplied by a special power source, which provides a background current to maintain the arc and adds the extra pulse at regular frequencies. The control given with this method reduces spatter and gives greater control of heat input to the workpiece. The amount of weld metal deposited can also be controlled to a much greater extent.

Dip Transfer

In this method, the wire electrode actually dips into the molten weld pool, causing a short circuit; at this point, the power source is designed to give an increase in current. The molten tip then melts off the electrode into the weld pool and the arc is re-established. This process results in a weld pool that solidifies relatively quickly, allowing positional welding and the welding of thinner sheet to be accomplished. These factors make it useful for motor vehicle body repair and sheet metal constructions.

Operating Procedures

There are a wide range of different types of welding machines for MAGS welding, so it is not possible to give specific instructions for all types. The following information is therefore for guidance only, although it is hoped that it will provide the basics when linked together with the information for the specific machine on which you are working.

The plate edge preparations for MAGS welding are the same as those used for manual metal arc welding.

Arc Voltage and Welding Current

It is best to set the open circuit voltage to the lowest setting giving the required arc voltage. If the arc voltage is set too high, there will be a tendency for the arc to be too long, with irregular metal transfer and consequently poor deposit quality with excessive spatter. Too low an arc voltage can result in 'stubbing' of the electrode wire into the weld pool or excessive penetration, or both. The detrimental effects of too high or too low an arc voltage will be more noticeable with dip transfer. Setting the welding current is achieved with the wire feed speed control. This is calibrated in different ways on different makes and types of machine.

Electrode Wire Size

Generally speaking, the smaller-diameter wires will give greater current density, resulting in a fast burn-off rate and a tendency to give deeper penetration welds.

Modern MAGS welding machines have an automatic inductance, but older machines can require a manual setting. The inductance is used when dip transfer welding, and the effect of increasing the inductance for any given open-circuit voltage is to produce a hotter arc which results in quieter welding conditions with less spatter and a smoother weld finish. If the inductance is decreased the arc will be cooler, giving out a distinctive 'crackling' sound and a weld surface with a more pronounced ripple.

On machines that require manual adjustment, high inductance will be needed for thicker materials and a low inductance setting for thin sheet.

Contact Tips and Nozzles

On some torches and guns, the position of the contact tip and nozzle are adjustable in order to allow for greater visibility of the welding area or accessibility to the particular joint, and/or improved gas shielding. The following settings are commonly recommended:

Mode of metal transfer	Recommended position of contact tip
Dip	3 mm to 9 mm beyond the end of the nozzle to allow greater visibility/accessibility
Spray (on steels)	6 mm to 9 mm within the nozzle to give improved gas shielding
Spray (on aluminium)	9 mm to 12 mm within the nozzle to give improved gas shielding
Spray (using flux-cored wire)	9 mm to 18 mm within the nozzle to give improved gas shielding and contact tube protection

The correct size of contact tip should always be used. A brief spray with silicone 'anti-spatter' solution before use and at regular intervals during use will aid the removal of spatter from the nozzle and tip. Nozzle and tip should be cleaned at regular intervals.

Perfection with MAGS welding, as with the other processes discussed in this book, will come with adequate practice under guidance.

Obtaining the correct welding speed is one area that requires special attention when learning MAGS welding. Too fast a welding speed can cause excessive spatter and undercut. Porosity may also be present owing to shielding gas being trapped in the quickly solidifying weld metal. Too slow a welding speed may cause excessive penetration.

The length that the electrode wire extends beyond the contact tip can also affect weld quality. The arc current will be reduced with increased amount of wire protruding, and this will result in less penetration. Wire extension from the contact tip should be approximately:

For dip transfer: 3 mm to 6 mm
For spray transfer: 18 mm to 30 mm
For flux-cored wire: 30 mm to 45 mm

Purging of the Torch or Gun

If the equipment has been left for any length of time, the gas hose and gun should be purged of any air before the welding equipment is used. Usually there is a gas purge button on the welding equipment. When this is pressed, shielding gas should flow through the hose and nozzle for approximately 15 seconds.

Some Possible Problems and Remedies

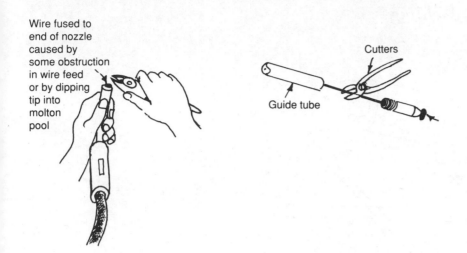

Wire fused to end of nozzle caused by some obstruction in wire feed or by dipping tip into molton pool

Cutters

Guide tube

Dealing with a 'burn-back'

Sometimes, the electrode wire can fuse to the contact tube. This is called a 'burn-back' and if it occurs, the torch trigger should be released at once, otherwise the drive rolls will continue to feed the wire and it will end up in a tangle around the wire feed mechanism. Sometimes the fused piece of wire can be removed easily, in other instances it may require sawing or grinding to free it. A badly damaged contact tube or tip should be replaced. The cause of the problem should be traced and cured (with supervised help if necessary).

Many welding problems can be caused by the use of the incorrect shielding gas, incorrect wire or unclean plate, so these points should be checked first if the desired results are not being obtained.

Although the process does not produce a slag like manual metal arc welding, it does form a thin silicate layer which must be removed when carrying out high-quality multi-run welds, before the subsequent run is deposited. Failure to remove this thin film can result in porosity and other defects which will cause a weld to fail radiographic standards. Lack of shielding gas will give major defects, as the weld will be a 'bare wire deposit' with no protection from the atmosphere. For this reason, the nozzle should be frequently cleaned of spatter deposits and welding should take place in a draught-free area. Obviously you should also check that there is an adequate supply of gas in the cylinder.

⚠	**SAFETY**

Switch off machine to carry out this operation.

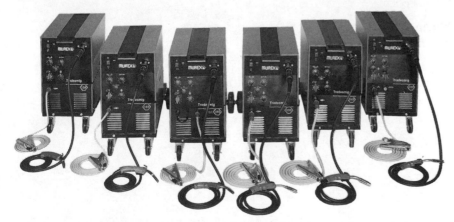

A range of air cooled MAGS machines. The wire spool is placed vertically with this type of equipment. Access is obtained by lifting off the side panel. (Courtesy of Murex Welding Products Ltd)

Welding Technique – Example Procedures

Bead on Plate by Dip Transfer Welding

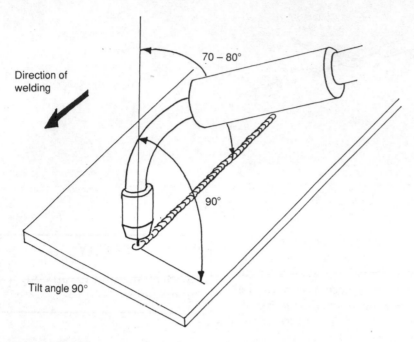

Recommended welding gun angles for forehand MAGS technique

1. Using either a 1.0 mm or a 1.2 mm diameter electrode, set the open-circuit voltage to around 25 volts.
2. Set inductance (if fitted) to mid-point and wire feed speed to about 4.25 metres per minute.
3. Set the carbon dioxide shielding gas flow at 9.0 to 12.0 litres per minute.
4. Selecting a piece of scrap 6 mm low carbon steel plate, deposit a weld bead, holding the gun at the angles shown in the sketch. The end of the nozzle should be about 10–15 mm from the work.
5. If the electrode stubs into the weld pool, increase the voltage slightly.
6. Examine the weld bead. If it is too small, increase the wire feed speed; or if the bead is too large, decrease the wire feed speed.

If the weld bead is 'peaky' in appearance, then increase the voltage.
Lack of fusion at the edges of the weld can be cured by increasing the voltage and/or the inductance.

MAGS welding is ideally suited to thin sections such as car bodywork. Here a weld is being made between two halves of a front wing using small clamps known as 'intergrips' to align the parts. (Courtesy of Frost Auto Restoration Techniques Ltd, Rochdale)

⚠ **SAFETY**

When electric welding on a car, the battery should be removed and, depending on the area being welded, it is also recommended that the petrol tank be removed and stored away from welding operations. Alternators should also be disconnected to avoid damage. Always have a fire extinguisher handy.

101

3 mm Butt Weld (Close and Open Square Edge) in the Flat Position

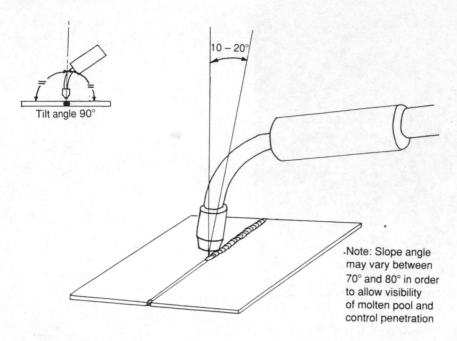

Tilt angle 90°

10 – 20°

.Note: Slope angle
may vary between
70° and 80° in order
to allow visibility
of molten pool and
control penetration

1. Assemble the plates using small tacks at the ends. The open square edge preparation should have a gap of 3 mm.
2. Adjust the contact tube to the work distance (electrode extension) and travel speed to control penetration. Electrode extension should not be greater than 1.5 cm.
3. Deposit the weld in one pass, at a speed fast enough to prevent weld metal flowing ahead of the arc.
4. If there is excessive reinforcement, reduce the wire feed speed and adjust the voltage and inductance to suit.

Tee Fillet Welds and Lap Welds in the Flat and Horizontal/Vertical Positions

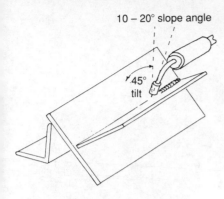

'T' fillet flat position

Assemble the joint without a gap at the joint line. Tack on one side and deposit weld on the untacked side of the joint. Contact tube to work distance should be kept at about 1.5 cm, and the gun should be held at the approximate angles shown.

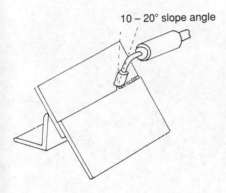

Lap weld flat position

Tilting of plates allows welding to be carried out in the flat position. This means that, generally, fewer runs are required, larger-diameter electrode wires may be used and the weld can be completed in a shorter time. All of these factors can reduce the overall cost of the job.

> **! NOTE**
>
> Slope and tilt angles are the same for laps and fillets.

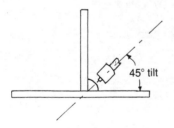

'T' fillet horizontal/vertical position

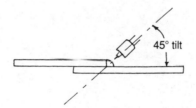

Lap weld horizontal/vertical position

Automatic Welding

Many automatic welding processes are employed in industry. MAGS welding, for instance, lends itself to robotics, in that a semi-automatic torch can be mounted on to a robot arm. In other applications, work can be moved beneath a fixed welding head or the head can be mounted on wheels and moved along a track alongside the work.

Resistance spot welding has been widely automated and robotised in recent years for mass production work such as the manufacture of car bodies and domestic appliances.

One automatic process which has been in use for many years where high-quality welds are required is the submerged arc process. This process gets its name because the arc is submerged underneath a powdered flux. Hand-held torches can be obtained for fillet and corner welds, but the process is more usually used in its automatic form for large high-quality welds on pressure vessels (where the work can be rotated beneath a fixed welding head), and bridges and girder work (where the welding head can be moved along a track next to the work).

Robotic MAGS welding. (MAGS welding lends itself to automation on certain types of work.)
(Courtesy of TWI, Cambridge)

The Submerged Arc Welding Process

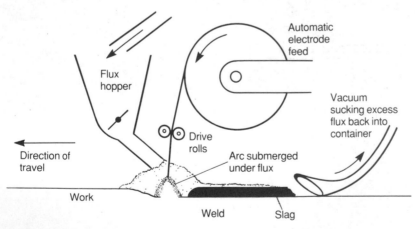

In this process, the bare wire electrode maintains an arc with the parent metal. The whole of the welding area is submerged under a powdered flux, which melts as the welding progresses along the seam. The flux forms a slag over the completed weld, further protecting it from the atmosphere. Any unburnt flux is returned to the flux hopper for re-use via a vacuum and filter system.

104

Test Your Knowledge

1. What type of power sources are usually used for MAGS welding?

2. State the electrode polarity normally used when MAGS welding.

3. What is the purpose of a heater when fitted to a carbon dioxide cylinder regulator.

4. Name two shielding gases other than carbon dioxide which may be used with the MAGS welding process.

5. What is the purpose of a pressure regulator and flowmeter?

6. Make a sketch to show the dip mode of metal transfer (five stages).

10 | RESISTANCE WELDING

Basic Principles of the Resistance Welding Process

The basic principle is that heat is generated when an electric current passes through an electrical resistance. The amount of heat generated depends on the amount of *current*, the amount of *resistance* and how long the current flows – *time*.

This basic resistance welding principle is expressed by the equation:

$$H = I^2RT$$

in which

H = the heat generated in joules
I^2 = the current flow in amperes squared
R = the resistance in ohms
T = the time the current flows in seconds

In words this means, the heat generated in a resistance weld is equal to the square of the current flowing through the workpiece, multiplied by the resistance of the workpieces, multiplied by the time that the current flows. From this it can be seen that if one of the three factors – current, resistance or time – is increased and the other two factors remain constant, the amount of heat produced is increased.

A factor K can be added to the formula to represent heat losses:

$H = I^2RTK$ when K has a constant value of 0.238

Uses of Resistance Welding

The economy and speed of resistance welding are especially valuable in mass production. The automotive industry is a prime example. Articles manufactured for use in the preparation and serving of food and the aircraft industry are others.

Spot Welding

The two pieces of plate (or thin sheet) are lapped and placed between the copper electrodes ②. Pressure is applied to ensure good physical and electrical contact. An electric current is passed through the electrodes and through the workpiece. The greatest amount of resistance, and therefore heat, is generated at the interface ③ directly in line with the electrodes. At this point, melting (in small areas) takes place. The molten area grows in size until the current is switched off. Electrode pressure is maintained until the molten

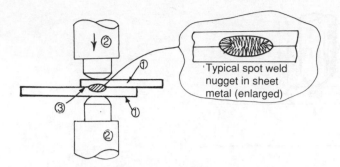

Typical spot weld nugget in sheet metal (enlarged)

metal cools. When it solidifies it forms a *weld nugget*. It is also important to establish the correct pressure between the electrodes to maximise the current flow without deformation.

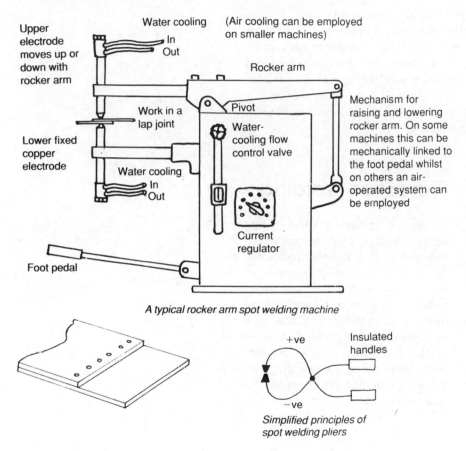

Upper electrode moves up or down with rocker arm

Water cooling
In
Out

(Air cooling can be employed on smaller machines)

Rocker arm

Work in a lap joint

Pivot

Water-cooling flow control valve

Mechanism for raising and lowering rocker arm. On some machines this can be mechanically linked to the foot pedal whilst on others an air-operated system can be employed

Lower fixed copper electrode

Water cooling
In
Out

Current regulator

Foot pedal

A typical rocker arm spot welding machine

+ve

Insulated handles

−ve

Simplified principles of spot welding pliers

The metal to be joined is placed between the electrodes in the form of a lap joint. The foot pedal is depressed, bringing the top electrode down on the work. The electric current, while having a low voltage, can be up to 80,000 amps (some automatic machines can use an amperage up to 200,000 amps). The minute air gaps between the two pieces of metal to be welded are sufficient to cause a resistance to the passage of electricity.

This resistance creates enough heat to melt the metal to form the spot weld.

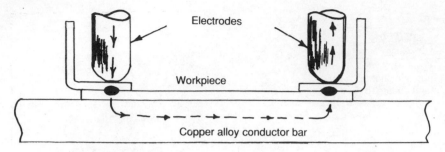

Series spot welding

Seam Welding

With ordinary spot welding it is not possible to place welds very close to each other as the current can pass through the first weld instead of through the interface to form the second weld. Seam welding is similar to spot welding, but the electrodes are a revolving set of wheels and the work is passed between them. A series of electrical impulses is sent through the electrodes which causes a number of spot welds to take place very close together or half overlapping each other, if required, to produce an air- or liquid-tight joint (which is not possible with normal spot welding).

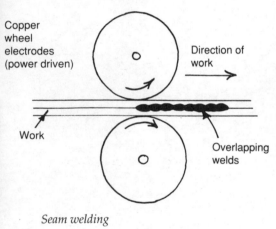

Seam welding

Projection Welding

Similar equipment is used in this process to that used in spot welding, except that the electrodes are flat copper platens. It is common for three or four projection welds to be made at once. A weld will be made at each projection. The projections are either pressed into one of the components as a separate operation prior to welding or forged in manufacture, as in the case of the nut.

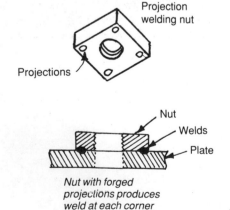

Nut with forged projections produces weld at each corner

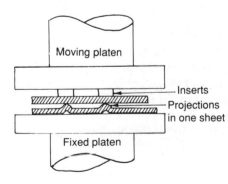

Projection welding

Resistance Butt Welding

Resistance butt welding is similar to resistance spot welding, but the actual components to be joined become the electrodes.

The two components are placed in the jaws of a machine and pressed together. A large current is passed through the work, bringing the ends to be joined up to welding heat. At this stage, extra force is applied and the ends are pushed together. At the point of welding, an enlargement of section takes place; this is called an 'upset' and can be removed by machining if required.

See also Chapter 11, the sections on Heat and temperature and Energy and work.

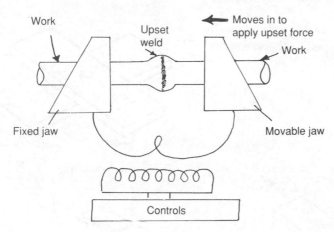
Flash Butt Welding

Although this is not strictly a resistance welding process, it is usually discussed within such processes as it is similar to resistance butt welding.

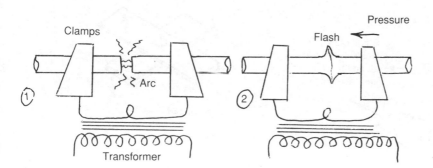

The components are brought together and a current passing through them heats the ends to red heat (because of resistance). The components are then separated a short distance and an electric arc is established between the ends until melting commences. At this point, the components are pushed together under high pressure with the current still flowing. This forms a ridge or 'flash' at the point of weld. Any impurities are forced out of the joint in the flash. Pressure and current are then switched off, although a post-weld heat treatment can be given after welding by again passing a controlled current through the work.

Testing

Common Defects in Spot Welding, and Destructive Tests

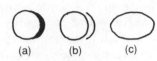

(a) Skid (b) Eyebrow
(c) Elliptical spot
These defects are usually caused by movement or sliding between the work-pieces and/or the electrodes, and incorrect alignment of the workpieces and/or the electrodes.

X-rays can be used to determine the quality of spot welds, but generally one or more of the following destructive tests is employed to check welding procedure.

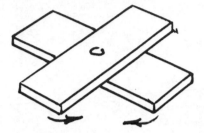

Twisting or torsion test

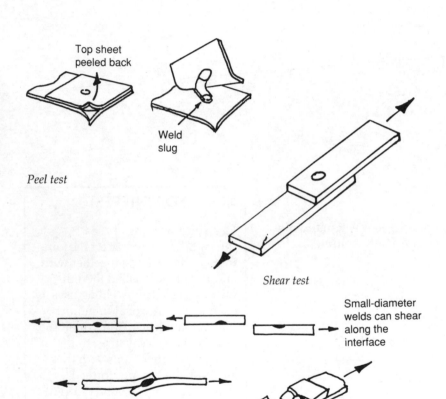

Peel test

Shear test

Small-diameter welds can shear along the interface

Larger-diameter welds can tear around the slug and through the material

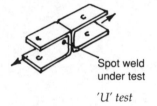

Spot weld under test

'U' test

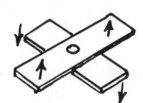

Cross tensile test

Lack of fusion is due to the following causes:
(a) Insufficient current
(b) Insufficient time
(c) Insufficient pressure
(d) Dirty work surfaces on plates to be joined, causing poor electrical contact and creating total current resistance.

Left: Basic pedal-operated spot welder (17 or 25 kVA). Right: Top of the range 'Stronghold' spot welder with Micropak 16p control (17/100/150 kVA). (Courtesy of British Federal)

Test Your Knowledge

1. What are the three main factors which cause heat to be produced for the resistance welding of metals?

2. Which type of resistance welding is best suited to produce an air- or liquid-tight joint?

3. Give one application for the use of projection welding.

4. How does resistance seam welding differ from resistance spot welding?

5. When does it become economically viable to use resistance welding methods of joining materials?

As the name of this chapter implies, it contains information that is necessary for a better understanding of welding. This section also includes some basic, welding related calculations.

Heat and Temperature

Because fusion welding involves large amounts of heat and high temperatures, the welder needs to understand the difference between *heat* and *temperature*.

In the welding workshop, the experienced welder can often judge the temperature of the work by the colour change of the metal, or special crayon sticks can be used which change colour at specific temperatures. For very accurate work, special temperature-measuring instruments called *pyrometers* can be used. The point to remember is that when we measure the temperature of a substance, we are not measuring the amount of heat it possesses.

The molecules (see the section on the structure of matter) in a hot substance move faster than those in a cold one, and temperature is a measurement of the degree of molecular motion in a substance. The amount of heat, however, is related to the mass of a substance or object, as well as its temperature. A substance with a large mass at a low temperature could contain a greater amount of heat than a smaller mass of the same substances at a high temperature.

In simple terms, if a pin head was heated to 650°C, the heat given off in a large room would go unnoticed. However, a block of steel 1 metre square at 550°C would be giving out a considerable amount of heat.

Scales of Temperature

The sketch shows a Centigrade or Celsius thermometer, named after the Swedish scientist Anders Celsius who put forward his ideas of using the freezing point of water as 0°C and the boiling point as 100°C in the year 1742.

The simple glass thermometer works by the expansion of either mercury or coloured alcohol, which rises or falls in the narrow tube which has calibrations along the side. Glass thermometers have a limited range of use and would, of course, melt at welding temperatures.

In winter, when temperatures can fall below zero, they have to be shown on the Celsius scale as minus figures. To avoid this, the Fahrenheit scale was devised by Gabriel Fahrenheit, a Dutch scientist. The Fahrenheit scale places the freezing point of water at 32°F and the boiling point at 212°F. In 1848, it was suggested by Lord Kelvin that the most logical starting point for a temperature scale would be absolute zero, called 0, and that all other temperatures could be measured from this point in degrees equal in magnitude to

A Celsius thermometer

degrees Celsius. This scale is now the SI (International Standard) scale and the unit of temperature is called the Kelvin (K). On the Kelvin, or Absolute scale as it is sometimes called, absolute zero is 0 K, the freezing point of water is 273.16 K and the boiling point of water is 373.16 K.

Energy and Work

Energy and work are connected, work being the expenditure of energy. They are therefore both measured in the same units, the SI unit being the joule, named after James Prescott Joule, the British physicist who showed that different forms of energy could be converted into each other without loss or gain of energy.

Because heat is energy it is measured in joules (J). As stated earlier, the amount of heat taken up by a substance depends on its mass and temperature. The final temperature will depend on the substance's specific heat capacity (specific heat capacity is measured by giving a substance of known mass a known amount of heat and measuring its rise in temperature).

As an example, a piece of copper will gain 50 K in temperature when receiving the same quantity of heat that will produce a rise of only 5 K in the same mass of water. Copper has, therefore, a specific heat capacity ten times that of water.

Conduction, Convection and Radiation

These are the three ways in which heat can travel from one place to another. They are important because they are methods of producing heat in the area to be welded with different welding processes, and they must be understood to appreciate how a weld loses heat.

Conduction

You have experienced conduction if you have ever burnt your fingers by picking up a piece of hot metal with your hand or mistakenly touched some metal that has just been welded.

Conduction is the flow of heat through solids. If one end of a solid is heated, the molecules at that end will start to vibrate faster and this vibrating action gradually moves through the solid if the heating is maintained.

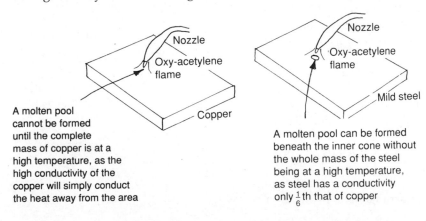

A molten pool cannot be formed until the complete mass of copper is at a high temperature, as the high conductivity of the copper will simply conduct the heat away from the area

A molten pool can be formed beneath the inner cone without the whole mass of the steel being at a high temperature, as steel has a conductivity only $\frac{1}{6}$th that of copper

Therefore, if you pick up a piece of metal that has just been welded, with your fingers instead of using tongs, the heat will flow into your fingertips and give a burning sensation. The rate at which heat is conducted is called thermal conductivity.

Convection

If you place your hand about 150 mm above a weld that has just been deposited, you will feel a lot of heat rising from it. This kind of heat transfer is known as convection. The recently deposited weld warms the air next to it. The air expands and becomes less dense than the surrounding air. It therefore rises from the hot weld and colder air will come in to replace it. This too will be heated and the cycle will be repeated until the weld cools down completely. Convection also takes place in liquids – as a pan of water is heated, convection currents in the water will stir it so that heating will automatically occur evenly throughout the water.

Radiation

A cooling weld will give off radiated heat energy, but the heat is transferred in a different way from conduction and convection.

Probably the best way of explaining radiation is to imagine standing in front of an open log fire. You will feel the warmth but it is not by convection because the air heated by the fire will be rising up the chimney. It cannot be by conduction either, because there is an air gap between you and the fire. The heat, in this instance, is produced by heat rays from the fire moving through the air and warming everything that absorbs them.

An understanding of the above three methods of heat transfer is essential when considering practical welding problems such as heat input to control distortion, methods of controlling cooling rate, fume extraction systems, protective equipment for welders and methods of cooling welding plant.

When welding, the effect of thermal conductivity can be best appreciated by considering two components of equal mass, one of copper and one of steel.

Structure of Matter.

The basic structure of matter is described in terms of atoms and molecules.

A substance which cannot be broken down into any simpler substances is called an *element*. There are, at this present moment in time, over 100 known elements, 92 of which are naturally occurring. Substances such as iron, aluminium, copper, oxygen and argon are all *elements*.

A substance which can be decomposed into two or more elements is known as a *compound*.

An *atom* is the smallest part of an element that can exist chemically. An atom consists of a number of negatively charged particles called electrons which surround a small dense nucleus of positive charge. The electrons experience an attraction due to the positive charge of the nucleus and orbit in regions of space around the nucleus.

Chemical compounds are made up of atoms and the nature of the compound is determined by the number, nature and arrangement of the atoms.

An atom is made up of three types of elementary particles: proton, electrons and neutrons.

The *proton* is a positively charged particle with a charge equal and opposite to the charge on an electron. It forms a constituent part of the nucleus of all atoms. The simplest nucleus is that of the hydrogen atom, which contains one proton.

The *electron* is 1/1836 of the mass of a proton. The electron's negative charge is equal but opposite to the charge on the proton. Electrons form a cloud around the nucleus and move within the electric field of the positive charge, being arranged in layers or shells.

The *neutron* has a mass equal to that of the proton but carries no electrical charge. It is a constituent part of all atomic nuclei except that of hydrogen.

The *atomic number* of an element indicates the number of protons in the nucleus and, because an atom in its normal state will exhibit no external charge, it will be the same as the number of electrons in the shells.

A *molecule* is the smallest part of a substance which can exist in a free state and yet will exhibit all the properties of the substance. Molecules of some elements like iron, copper and aluminium contain only one atom and are called monatomic. Molecules of other elements such as oxygen, hydrogen and nitrogen consist of two atoms and are called diatomic. A molecule of the compound carbon dioxide contains three atoms, and other complicated compounds contain many atoms.

Isotopes are forms of an element which possess some of the element's chemical properties but differ in atomic mass. The atomic weight of an isotope is known as its mass number. As an example, carbon in one form has 6 protons and 6 neutrons in its nucleus, which gives an atomic number of 6. Other carbon atoms exist, however, with 7 neutrons and 8 neutrons in the nucleus. These are called isotopes and their mass numbers will be 13 and 14 respectively, compared with a mass number of 12 for the normal carbon atom. Heavy hydrogen or deuterium has a mass number of 2; this means that it has one proton and one neutron in its nucleus.

Nature of Matter

It is now believed that all matter on Earth and quite possibly in the Universe is built up of many pure substances known as elements.

The Various States of Matter

As a solid, liquid or gas, the ultimate particle making up a substance is the atom. The atom has a positively charged nucleus surrounded by negatively charged electrons.

The number of electrons in orbit around the nucleus determines the nature and stability of the atom, and the chemical and physical characteristics of the substance itself.

Molecules

A molecule is the smallest possible particle of a compound formed by two or more atoms, depending on the type of matter.

In a solid substance, the molecules have a great attraction for each other.

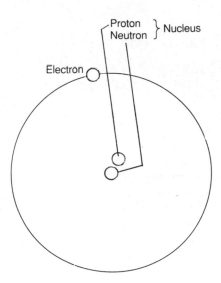

The neutron has no charge
The proton has a positive charge
The electron has a negative charge

Substances that have a definite molecular pattern are called crystalline. In liquids and gases the molecular attraction is much less and these substances are said to be amorphous (having no fixed crystalline shape or pattern).

The three states of matter – solids, liquids and gases – are closely related, for it is only by giving or taking away heat that we can change matter from one state to another.

Ice, water and steam are typical examples of the three changes of state within a substance caused by changing temperature.

Matter cannot be destroyed, it can only be changed.

Elements, Mixtures and Compounds

Elements

An element is the simplest form of a substance which cannot be split up into anything simpler. There are two types of element: metals and non-metals. 92 elements occur naturally and some others are man-made.

The surface of the earth consists of approximately:

50% Oxygen (in compound form)	O
26% Silicon	Si
7% Aluminium	Al
4% Iron	Fe
3% Calcium	Ca

Common Metallic Elements

Aluminium	Al	
Copper	Cu	
Tin	Sn	
Lead	Pb	These are all pure metals.
Iron	Fe	
Gold	Au	
Silver	Ag	

Common Gaseous Elements

Oxygen	O	
Nitrogen	N	The Earth's atmosphere is
Hydrogen	H	made up mostly of nitrogen
Helium	He	and oxygen (approximately
Argon	A	$4/_5$ N and $1/_5$ O).

Some Common Non-metallic Elements

Carbon	C
Calcium	Ca
Phosphorus	P
Sulphur	S
Silicon	Si

Examples of Common Reactions

Elements	Result of reaction
Sulphur + Iron + Heat	Iron sulphide
Carbon + Iron + Heat	Iron carbide (Cementite)
Calcium + Carbon + Heat	Calcium carbide

In all the above reactions, heat is the catalyst. If no heat was present, the elements would not have combined chemically and they would have remained as a mixture.

Iron + Oxygen (Fe + O) will produce the compound Fe_3O_4 (rust) only if water vapour is present, so in this instance water is the catalyst. Rust is the compound of iron oxide (Fe_3O_4). The reaction will take place faster as the temperature is increased.

Mixtures

These occur when two or more elements are mixed together with no reaction taking place. A mixture maintains the chemical and physical characteristics of its component parts, that is, their appearance, smell, taste etc. A mixture can easily be separated back into its component parts. Examples are:

Mixture	Method of separation
Salt and Water	Boil off water and condense. A residue of salt remains
Iron and Sulphur	Pass a magnet over the mixture to remove iron
Salt and Silica	Add water – the salt will dissolve into the water leaving the silica. Boil water to retrieve salt

Molecules are composed of atoms, and the number of atoms in each molecule depends on the substance; for example, iron sulphide, which has one atom of iron and one atom of sulphur per molecule chemically combined. This would be written as: $Fe + S \rightarrow FeS$.

Some molecules have more than one atom; for example, oxygen has two (O_2), as has hydrogen (H_2).

Compounds

These are elements which combine chemically to form new substances which can often have completely different chemical and physical properties from the original elements. For example:

Hydrogen + Oxygen $\rightarrow$ Water   Sodium + Chloride $\rightarrow$ Salt
Oxygen + Silicon $\rightarrow$ Sand   Carbon + Hydrogen $\rightarrow$ Acetylene

Metallic Alloys

In cases where high electrical conductivity or maximum ductility are required, metals in their pure state are often used. However, when mechanical properties such as tensile strength and hardness are needed, these and other properties can be improved by adding two or more metals together to form *alloys*. For example:

Copper + Zinc = Brass	Various percentages and additions
Iron + Carbon = Steel	of other alloying elements will vary
Aluminium + Copper = Duralumin	the properties of alloys considerably.

EXTRACT FROM THE TABLE OF ELEMENTS:

Element	Symbol	Atomic weight	Melting point in °C
Aluminium	Al	26.97	658.7
Antimony	Sb	121.77	630
Argon	Ar	39.94	−188
Arsenic	As	74.96	850
Beryllium	Be	9.02	1280
Bismuth	Bi	209.00	271
Boron	B	10.82	2200–2500
Cadmium	Cd	112.41	320.9
Calcium	Ca	40.07	810
Carbon	C	2.00	3600
Chlorine	Cl	35.45	−101.5
Chromium	Cr	52.01	1615
Cobolt	Co	58.94	1480
Copper	Cu	63.57	1083
Fluorine	F	19.0	−223
Gold	Au	197.2	1063
Helium	He	4.0	−272
Hydrogen	H	1.0078	−259
Iron	Fe	55.84	1530
Lead	Pb	207.22	327.4
Magnesium	Mg	24.32	651
Manganese	Mn	54.93	1230
Mercury	Hg	200.61	−38.87
Molybdenum	Mo	96	2620
Neon	Ne	20.18	−253
Nickel	Ni	8.69	452
Niobium (Columbium)	Nb (Cb)	92.9	1950
Nitrogen	N	14.008	−210
Oxygen	O	16.000	−218
Phosphorus	P	30.98	44
Platinum	Pt	195.23	1755
Potassium	K	391	62.3
Silicon	Si	28.06	1420
Silver	Ag	107.88	960.5
Sodium	Na	22.99	97.5
Sulphur	S	32.06	112.8
Thorium	Th	232.12	1700
Tin	Sn	118.70	231.9
Titanium	Ti	47.9	1800
Tungsten	W	184.0	3400
Uranium	U	238.14	1850
Vanadium	V	50.96	1720
Xenon	Xe	131.3	−140
Zinc	Zn	65.38	419.4
Zirconium	Zr	91.22	1700

The Oxy-Acetylene Welding Flame

When oxygen and acetylene are mixed together in a blowpipe in approximately equal proportions, a blue, non-luminous flame is produced at the nozzle. The brightest part is the blue inner cone. The temperature of this flame, measured just in front of the inner cone, is approximately 3,250°C.

Approximate Temperatures of Various Flames

Oxy-acetylene 3,250°C
Oxy-butane (Calor-gas) 2,815°C
Oxy-propane (liquefied petroleum gas, LPG) 2,810°C
Oxy-methane (natural gas) 2,770°C
Oxy-hydrogen 2,820°C
Air-acetylene 2,320°C
Air-methane 1,850°C
Air-propane 1,900°C
Air-butane 1,800°C

The metal arc has been measured at 6 000°C and higher, depending on the type of arc.

Combustion of the Oxy-Acetylene Flame

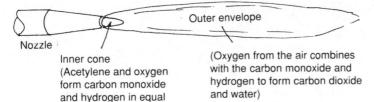

Nozzle

Inner cone
(Acetylene and oxygen form carbon monoxide and hydrogen in equal volumes)

Outer envelope

(Oxygen from the air combines with the carbon monoxide and hydrogen to form carbon dioxide and water)

The oxy-acetylene flame

Acetylene is composed of carbon and hydrogen (C_2H_2), and it burns in air with a black smoky flame, the smoke being due to incomplete combustion of the carbon:

acetylene + oxygen → carbon + water
$2C_2H_2$ + O_2 → 4C + $2H_2O$

If, however, a special burner is used, almost complete combustion can be obtained, and the acetylene will burn with a very brilliant flame, because of the incandescent carbon.

When acetylene and oxygen are passed through a welding blowpipe, they mix before reaching the nozzle. When this mixture is made up of equal volumes of the two gases, then complete combustion can take place when the mixture is ignited with the addition of $1\frac{1}{2}$ volumes of oxygen from the surrounding atmosphere to form a neutral flame.

The process of combustion occurs in two stages:
1. The first stage takes place in the blue, luminous cone, which is well defined when the flame is correctly adjusted and is known as the *inner cone*. In this

region, the acetylene combines with the oxygen supplied, forming carbon monoxide and hydrogen:

acetylene + oxygen $\rightarrow$ carbon monoxide + hydrogen
$$C_2H_2 + O_2 \rightarrow 2CO + H_2$$

2. The second stage of combustion is in the external zone, called the *outer envelope*. In this region, carbon monoxide burns and forms carbon dioxide, and the hydrogen which is formed from the first reaction combines with oxygen to form water:

carbon monoxide + hydrogen + oxygen $\rightarrow$ carbon dioxide + water
$$CO + H_2 + O_2 \rightarrow CO_2 + H_2O$$

With this reaction, the combustion is complete and the chief products are carbon dioxide and water, which is turned to steam.

The oxy-acetylene flame is a strong *reducing* agent, as it absorbs oxygen from the air into the outer envelope. This is another benefit of using this flame for welding purposes, for as well as having the highest working temperature, the tendency to form oxides while welding is greatly minimised.

For complete combustion, it is usual to have equal amounts of oxygen and acetylene being consumed. If there is more acetylene than oxygen, then combustion will be incomplete and the flame will give off free carbon. This type of flame is known as the carbonising or carburising flame.

If more oxygen is supplied than acetylene, then there is an excess of the amount required for complete combustion, and the flame is called an oxidising flame.

When welding low carbon steel, the neutral flame is used, having equal amounts of oxygen and acetylene. For other applications, either an oxidising or a carburising flame may be required. See section on the Three types of gas welding flame in Chapter 3.

The Properties of Metals

Different metals have different mechanical properties and the way they behave in service is greatly influenced by these properties.

The mechanical properties of interest to the engineer are:

Ductility

This term implies that a metal has the ability to be readily drawn into rod or wire. The ductility of a metal is determined by the amount it will stretch, lengthwise, before it becomes brittle and fails.

Because ductility reduces as the temperature of the metal is increased, metals are usually drawn in the cold state.

Plasticity

This measures the ability of a metal to be formed into a given shape without fracture. As very few metals are plastic in the cold state, heat is used in most cases when forming, to increase plasticity. There are odd exceptions to this, when an increase in temperature can cause brittleness in some metals.

Brittleness

This is the opposite of plasticity, it refers to the tendency of a metal to break suddenly when under load, without any appreciable deformation. Many metals in their cast state will fracture when subjected to a large enough impact. In some metals, an increase in temperature can reduce brittleness, while in others it can cause it to occur.

Malleability

This property allows a metal to be compressed without failure. It is necessary if forging or rolling operations are to be carried out. Most metals have a greater malleability when worked in the hot condition.

Hardness

This is generally defined as the ability of a metal to resist indentation or abrasion. The measurement of hardness is usually based on a metal's resistance to the indentation of either a hardened steel ball (the Brinell Hardness Test) or a diamond (Vickers or Rockwell Hardness Tests), although abrasion tests are used in some cases, such as the shot and sand blasting industries.

   Hardness can be increased by deformation caused by cold working, known as work hardening. In steels, carbon is the main hardening element and in many ferrous alloys, high levels of hardness can be obtained by heating the alloy to a high temperature followed by rapid cooling.

Tenacity

This is the property by virtue of which a body resists a deforming force. It is another name for the tensile strength of a material.

Toughness

This is a combination of ductility and tenacity – the property which enables a material to resist fracture by bending, twisting or shock.

Brief Summary of the Effects of Elevated Temperatures on the Mechanical Properties of Metals

Plasticity

This will usually increase with rise in temperature. Iron and steel are difficult to bend in the cold state, but bend easily when red hot. Wrought iron is also plastic, but can sometimes break (because of impurities) when red hot.

Brittleness

Copper is a ductile metal but becomes brittle near its melting point. In general, most metals become *less* brittle when heat is applied. Special care should be taken when welding brittle metals because of their lack of ductility.

Malleability

This is the property of a metal being permanently flattened or stretched by hammering or rolling. The more malleable a metal is, the thinner the sheets into which it can be formed. Metals such as iron and steel become much more malleable with increased temperature. Copper is very malleable except near its melting point. Zinc is only malleable between 140°C and 160°C. Any impurities will reduce malleability. A rivet needs to be made of a malleable material in order to withstand the hammering.

Metals in order of malleability

Gold	Au
Silver	Ag
Aluminium	Al
Copper	Cu
Tin	Sn
Lead	Pb
Zinc	Zn
Iron	Fe

Ductility

In order for a metal to be ductile, the molecules must have a great attraction for each other after the yield point has been passed. As the molecules have a greater attraction for each other when cold, metals will be more ductile when cold. This is why wires and rods for the welding industry are drawn in the cold state.

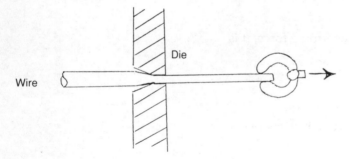

Wire needs to be ductile in order to be drawn through a die

Further Properties of Metals

Tensile Strength

This is the property that enables a metal to withstand a stretching load without breaking.

Compressive Strength

This is the property that enables a metal to withstand compressive loading without fracture.

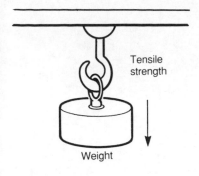

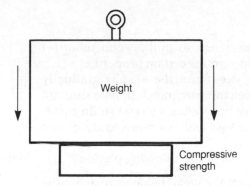

Tensile strength

Compressive strength

Shear Strength

This is the ability of a metal to withstand loads which are not in the same line of force (offset loads).

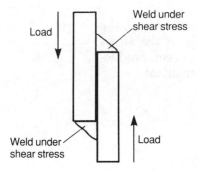

Impact Strength

This is the ability to withstand impact.

Elasticity

This is the ability of a metal to deform under load and then return to its original shape once the load has been removed. An example is a spring.

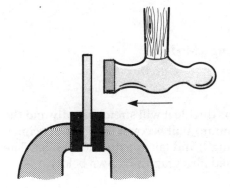

Plasticity

This is the ability of a metal to form a given shape, without fracture, and remain in that shape once the load has been removed. Coins are examples of plastic material.

Stress/Strain and Tensile Strength

A tensile testing machine is specially designed to pull specimens of set dimensions to breaking point in order to determine certain properties.

When the specimen is under tensile stress and the load is gradually increased until breaking point occurs, then the specimen will pass through certain phases. These phases can be shown by plotting a stress/strain curve. The curve is found by taking a number of load and extension readings and plotting stress against strain.

A line can be drawn on a graph and will show the following phases:

1. Limit of proportionality: Up to this point the metal behaves in an elastic manner and if the load were removed, the specimen would return to its original dimensions.
2. Yield point: The metal gives at this point, and if the load were removed the specimen would not return to its original dimensions.
3. Ultimate tensile strength: Here, the load is at the maximum that the specimen will take. If this point is exceeded, the metal becomes weaker until failure occurs.

If the extension (strain) is proportional to the applied load (stress), the metal is said to have obeyed Hooke's Law. For example, if the stress increases by 50 per cent, the strain will also increase by 50 per cent, producing a straight line which will indicate the elastic range of the material.

$$\text{Stress} = \frac{\text{Load}}{\text{Cross-sectional area}}$$

$$\text{Strain} = \frac{\text{Extension of gauge length}}{\text{Original gauge length}}$$

$$\text{Hooke's Law} = \frac{\text{Stress}}{\text{Strain}} = E$$

where E is a constant known as Young's Modulus.

The Breaking Point

As a metal approaches this point, if it is ductile it will stretch rapidly and the load required to stretch it a given amount will become less. The specimen will begin to 'waist' (known as 'necking'), and fail in a ductile manner. The load is applied and the extension plotted on a graph as shown below.

Stress/Strain Curve for a Ductile Material Such As Low Carbon Steel

From A to B the straight line indicates that the extension is proportional to the load. Between these points, the material still retains its *elasticity*, so that if the load were removed the specimen would return to its original length.

From B to C it can be seen that the metal extends with no increase in load. The specimen is said to have taken 'permanent set' and, if the load is removed at this stage, the metal will not return to its original length. This is known as the *yield point*.

From C to D the extension is no longer proportional to the load and, if the load is removed, little or no spring-back will occur. In this state the metal is said to be *plastic*.

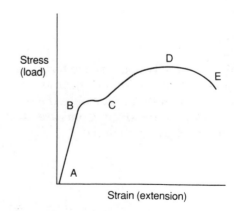

Point D is the ultimate tensile stress of the material and point E represents the breaking point. From point D to E the material appears to continue stretching under reduced load. In fact, the specimen, because it is a ductile material, is thinning out (necking), until it finally breaks at point E.

Ultimate Tensile Strength (UTS): To calculate the UTS of the metal, the maximum load indicated on the stress/strain curve (D) is divided by the original cross-sectional area. The UTS is mainly of use at the design stage.

Yield Stress: This is calculated by taking the load at point B and dividing by the original cross-sectional area of the specimen. It is usual for designers to work at 50 per cent of this figure to give a 'safety factor'.

Elongation Percentage: This is found by taking the increased length at fracture and dividing it by the original length. The resultant figure is expressed as a percentage and is an accurate indication of the materials *ductility*.

A brittle material will show little or no 'necking' and will fracture in a brittle manner, usually with a bang.

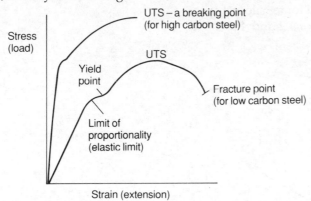

A comparison of a stress/strain curve for high carbon steel with that of a low carbon steel will show that the high carbon steel

1. Has a longer line of proportionality (elasticity).
2. Indicates a higher yield point load.
3. Has a higher ultimate tensile strength.
4. Shows less elongation.
5. The UTS and breaking point are together.

This comparison indicates that an increase in hardness will normally produce an increased tensile strength, but a reduction in ductility.

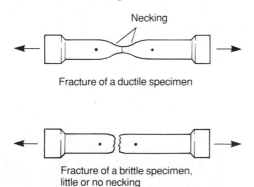

Necking

Fracture of a ductile specimen

Fracture of a brittle specimen, little or no necking

Example of All Weld Metal Tensile Specimen (for certain welding tests, specimens can be machined entirely from weld metal)

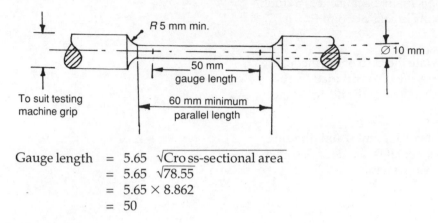

Gauge length = 5.65 $\sqrt{\text{Cross-sectional area}}$
= 5.65 $\sqrt{78.55}$
= 5.65 × 8.862
= 50

Example of Tensile Test Including Plate Material and Weld

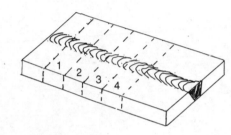

Depending on the code, sections 1 and 3 can be used for tensile test specimens, and sections 2 and 4 as bend test specimens.

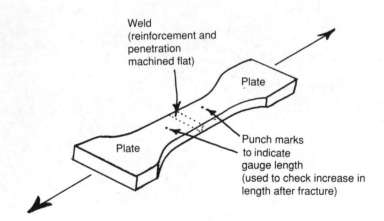

Exact dimensions of tensile specimens should be checked against the requirements of the welding code or standard being worked to.

Elementary Welding Drawing Symbols
(BS499, part 2, 1980)

Cross-section	Symbol	Description
1.	人	Butt weld between flanged plates (upturned edges), the flanges being melted down completely
2.	‖	Square butt weld
3.	V	Single-V butt weld
4.	V	Single-bevel butt weld
5.	Y	Single-V butt weld with broad root face
6.	Y	Single-bevel butt weld with broad root face
7.	Y	**Single-U butt weld**
8.	P	Single-J butt weld
9.	⌣	Backing or sealing run
10.	◺	Fillet weld
11.	⊓	Plug weld (circular or elongated hole, completely filled)
12.	○	Spot weld (resistance or arc welding), or projection weld
13.	⊖	Seam weld

Welding Drawing Symbols Extracted From BS499, part 2, 1980

To indicate the type of weld and the position of a weld on a drawing, the symbols are used in conjunction with an arrow line and reference line as shown.

Reference line   Symbol

Arrow line

Supplementary symbols:

Shape of weld surface	Symbol
Flat (usually finished flush)	———
Convex	⌒
Concave	⌣

Indication of size of weld:

b △   *a* is design throat thickness

ba △   *b* is leg length

Examples of the use of supplementary symbols:

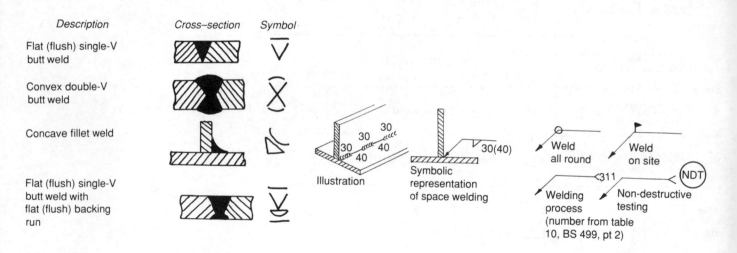

Description	Cross–section	Symbol
Flat (flush) single-V butt weld		
Convex double-V butt weld		
Concave fillet weld		
Flat (flush) single-V butt weld with flat (flush) backing run		

30 30 30
30 40 40

Illustration

Symbolic representation of space welding

30(40)

Weld all round   Weld on site

311

Welding process (number from table 10, BS 499, pt 2)   Non-destructive testing   NDT

Examples of the use of symbols

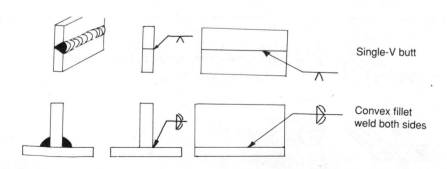

Single-V butt

Convex fillet weld both sides

128

Table 10.* Numerical indication of process

No.	Process	No.	Process
1	**Arc welding**	47	Gas pressure welding
11	Metal-arc welding without gas protection	48	Cold welding
111	*Metal-arc welding with covered electrode*		
112	Gravity arc welding with covered electrode	**7**	**Other welding processes**
113	Bare wire metal-arc welding	71	*Thermit welding*
114	Flux cored metal-arc welding	72	Electroslag welding
115	Coated wire metal-arc welding	73	Electrogas welding
118	Firecracker welding	74	Induction welding
12	Submerged arc welding	75	Light radiation welding
121	Submerged arc welding with wire electrode	751	Laser welding
122	Submerged arc welding with strip electrode	752	Arc image welding
13	Gas shielded metal-arc weldin	753	Infrared welding
131	*MIG welding*	76	Electron beam welding
135	MAG welding: metal-arc welding with non-inert gas shield	78	Stud welding
		781	Arc stud welding
136	Flux cored metal-arc welding with non-inert gas shield	78	Resistance stud welding
14	Gas-shielded welding with non-consumable electrode	**9**	**Brazing, soldering and braze welding**
141	*TIG welding*	91	*Brazing*
149	*Atomic-hydrogen welding*	911	Infrared brazing
15	Plasma arc welding	912	*Flame brazing*
18	Other arc welding processes	913	Furnace brazing
181	*Carbon arc welding*	914	Dip brazing
185	Rotating arc welding	916	Induction brazing
915	Salt bath brazing	917	Ultrasonic brazing
		918	Resistance brazing
		919	Diffusion brazing
2	**Resistance welding**	923	Vacuum brazing
21	*Spot welding*	924	Vacuum brazing
22	*Seam welding*	93	Other brazing processes
221	Lap seam welding	94	Soldering
225	Seam welding with strip	941	Infrared soldering
23	*Projection welding*	942	Flame soldering
24	*Flash welding*	944	Dip soldering
25	*Resistance butt welding*	945	Salt bath soldering
29	Other resistance welding processes	946	Induction soldering
29	HF resistance welding	947	Ultrasonic soldering
943	Furnace soldering	948	Resistance soldering
		949	Diffusion soldering
		951	Flow soldering
3	**Gas welding**	952	Soldering with soldering iron
31	Oxy-fuel gas welding		
311	*Oxy-acetylene welding*	954	Vacuum soldering
312	Oxy-propane welding	96	Other soldering processes
313	Oxy-hydrogen welding	322	Air-propane welding
32	Air fuel gas welding	971	Gas braze welding
321	Air-acetylene welding	72	Arc braze welding
97	*Braze welding*	441	Explosive welding
953	Friction soldering		
4	**Solid phase welding; pressure welding**		
41	Ultrasonic welding		
42	*Friction welding*		
43	Force welding		
44	Welding by high mechanical energy		
45	Diffusion welding		

* This table complies with International Standard ISO 4063.

Calculations Related To Welding (fractions, decimals, percentages, proportion and averages)

Fractions

A fraction is a quantity that is not a whole number. There are two kinds of fractions: *vulgar fractions*, which are usually referred to as *fractions* and *decimal fractions* which are usually just called *decimals*.

Vulgar fractions are shown by two numbers placed one above the other, being separated by a line. The number below the line is called the *denominator* and the number above the line is called the *numerator*.

The denominator shows how many parts (of equal size) the whole is divided up into, and the numerator shows how many of these parts are taken. For example: $\frac{3}{5}$ of 20 shows that twenty is divided into five equal parts and that three of these are taken. In other form this would be: $\frac{20}{5}$ (20 divided by 5 equal parts) $\times 3 = 4 \times 3 = 12$. Therefore $\frac{3}{5}$ of 20 = 12.

Proper fractions

Proper fractions are those which make up less than 1, such as: $\frac{3}{4}, \frac{1}{4}, \frac{1}{3}, \frac{2}{3}, \frac{1}{2}$, etc. – that is, when the numerator is less than the denominator.

Improper fractions

These are fractions that are greater than 1 – that is, the numerator is greater than the denominator. For example:

$$\frac{7}{6} = 1\frac{1}{6}, \quad \frac{9}{8} = 1\frac{1}{8}, \quad \frac{17}{4} = 4\frac{1}{4} \text{ etc.}$$

Decimal fractions

The decimal system enables calculations to be made more easily when using metric measurements.

Decimal fractions are shown by using a decimal point. The point is placed to the right of the unit and figures placed to the right of the point indicate tenths, hundredths, thousandths, etc., of a complete unit, depending on their place after the point. The first figure after the point represents tenths of a unit, the next hundredths, the next thousandths, and so on. Therefore

1.3 represents one and three tenths $\left(1 + \frac{3}{10}\right)$

$0.25 = \frac{2}{10} + \frac{5}{100} = \frac{25}{100}$

Decimals

This is the general term applied to the system of representing whole and fractional numbers in the base of ten. The decimal point is used to identify place values as shown in decimal fractions.

130

Worked Examples of Decimal Calculations

Addition:

```
        17·85
        10·20
         6·30  +
      ─────────
        34·35      Ans
      ─────────
```

Always keep the decimal points in line.

Subtraction:

```
        18·25
         8·41  −
      ─────────
         9·84      Ans
      ─────────
```

Multiplication:

```
         6·25
          6·2  ×
      ─────────
         1250
         3750
      ─────────
        38·750     Ans
      ─────────
```

The actual multiplication is done as if there were no decimal points. Then the total number of decimal places in the two numbers being multiplied together are counted (total number of digits to the *right* of the decimal point in the two numbers). Count from the right towards the left this number of places in the answer, and place the decimal point in that position.

Division:

```
             0·5266
          ──────────
        15) 7·90000
            7 5
          ──────
              40
              30
            ────
             100
              90
            ────
             100
              90
            ────
              10
```

Some calculations will not always finish exactly, so we can write the answer correct to a required number of decimal places. In the calculation shown, it would go on for ever, so we have stopped it, giving the answer correct to 4 decimal places.

Worked Examples of Fraction Calculations

Addition:

$$4\frac{1}{8} + 3\frac{7}{12} = 7\frac{3+14}{24} = 7\frac{17}{24}$$

24 is the lowest number that both 8 and 12 will divide into equally. 8 into 24 goes 3, $3 \times 1 = 3$. 12 into 24 goes twice, $2 \times 7 = 14$

Subtraction:

$$3\frac{3}{8} - 1\frac{7}{12} = 2_1\frac{9^{24} - 14}{24} = 1\frac{19}{24}$$

Again, 24 is the lowest common denominator.
8 divides equally three times, $3 \times 3 = 9$.
12 divides into 24 equally twice, $2 \times 7 = 14$.
In order to subtract 14 from 9, we have to take one whole number from the $2\ (\frac{24}{24})$.

Multiplication:

$$3\frac{3}{4} \times 1\frac{1}{9} = \frac{^515}{^24} \times \frac{^510}{^39} = \frac{25}{6} = 4\frac{1}{6}$$

The whole numbers and fractions are converted to improper fractions: $3\frac{3}{4}$ becomes $3 \times 4 = 12 + 3 = \frac{15}{4}$. $1\frac{1}{9}$ becomes $9 \times 1 = 9 + 1 = \frac{10}{9}$. On completing the calculation, the improper fraction of $\frac{25}{6}$ is changed to a whole number and proper fraction of, by dividing the denominator (6) into the numerator (25).

Division:

$$3\frac{3}{4} \div 1\frac{1}{9} = \frac{15}{4} \div \frac{10}{9} = \frac{^315}{4} \times \frac{9}{10_2} = \frac{27}{8} = 3\frac{3}{8}$$

Again, improper fractions are used and then we invert (turn upside down) and multiply after cancelling down. That is, 5 goes equally into 15, three times and into 10 twice.

Percentages

Percentage is a method of relating a fraction of a quantity to the whole in parts per hundred. For example:

20% is the same as $\frac{20}{100}$ (% means 'per cent')

From this, it can also be seen that 20% is the same as the fraction $\frac{1}{5}$ as 20 will divide into 20 once, and into 100 five times.

Percentage changes in any quantity are calculated in the following ways. If original value = A, and new value = B:

$$\text{per cent change} = \frac{A - B}{A} \times 100$$

Percentage equivalents of fractions are given by multiplying the fraction by 100. For example:

$$\frac{2}{5} = \frac{2}{5} \times 100\% = 40\%$$

$$\frac{2}{5_1} \times \frac{100^{20}}{1} = \frac{40}{1}$$

A percentage equivalent of a decimal is given by multiplying the decimal by 100. For example:

$$0.25 = 0.25 \times 100\% = 25\%$$

A *fraction* may be changed into a *decimal* by dividing the numerator by the denominator. For example:

$$\frac{1}{2} = 2\overline{\smash{)}1}^{\,0.5} = 0.5$$

$$\frac{3}{8} = 8\overline{\smash{)}3.000}^{\,0.375} = 0.375$$

Electrode Efficiency

When electric arc welding, the electrode efficiency is the mass of metal actually deposited compared with the mass of the core wire consumed. *Electrode efficiency* can be expressed as a percentage:

$$\text{Efficiency \%} = \frac{\text{Mass of deposited metal}}{\text{Mass of electrode metal consumed}} \times 100$$

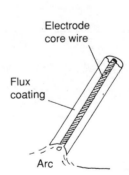

Electrode core wire

Flux coating

Arc

With general-purpose electrodes, the efficiency can vary between about 75% up to 90%. However, with electrodes that contain iron powder in the flux, covering efficiency levels can approach 200%.

Electrode efficiency (or recovery rates) are given to the nearest 10, in the electrode coding for a particular electrode (see BS639: (1986)).

The nominal electrode efficiency percentage is given by:

$$\frac{\text{mass of deposited metal}}{\text{mass of core wire} - \text{mass of unused stub}} = \text{percentage recovery}$$

Fractions and Decimals

The shaded parts of the squares represent:

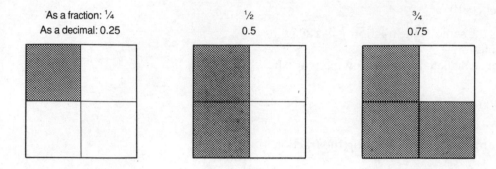

| As a fraction: ¼ | ½ | ¾ |
| As a decimal: 0.25 | 0.5 | 0.75 |

Distances represented as fractions and decimals on a given weld length of 160 mm:

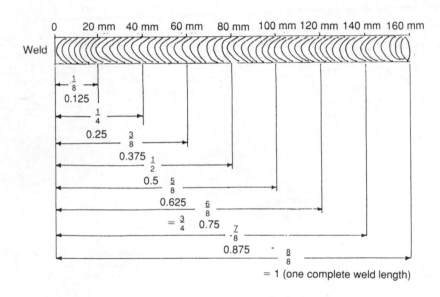

Ratio and Proportion

As an example, suppose a welder earns £5 per hour, and saves £2. Then it can be said that the *ratio* of hourly savings to earnings is 2 to 5. This is sometimes written as 2:5.

The ratio can be expressed in the form of a fraction, $\frac{2}{5}$. The ratio of earnings to savings is 5 to 2, 5:2 or $\frac{5}{2}$

$\frac{2}{5}$ and $\frac{5}{2}$ are called *inverse ratios*.

If, the welder's wages were increased to £5.50 per hour, and he saved £2.50 per hour of this, then the ratio of savings to earnings would be:

$2\frac{1}{2}$ to $5\frac{1}{2}$ which is the same as 5 to 11

Direct proportion

If an automatic welding machine is welding heavy plate at the rate of 12 metres per hour, then the following statements could be made:

Welding 12 metres in 60 minutes
ratio of distance to time $= \frac{12}{60} = \frac{1}{5}$

Welding 6 metres in 30 minutes
ratio of distance to time $= \frac{6}{30} = \frac{1}{5}$

Welding 4 metres in 20 minutes
ratio of distance to time $= \frac{4}{20} = \frac{1}{5}$

Welding 1 metre in 5 minutes
ratio of distance to time $= \frac{1}{5}$

In each case, the ratio of welding distance (in metres) to time (in minutes) is equal to $\frac{1}{5}$.

When two ratios have the same value, the four quantities making up the ratios are said to be 'in proportion'. In the example shown above, the times and distances are in proportion.

In working out proportions, we assume that only the amounts being dealt with at the time vary and that everything else stays the same. An example of this would be to say that a welder's wages are proportional to the number of hours worked. Here, we are assuming that the rate of pay per hour is the constant, and ignoring the fact that some of the hours are being paid at overtime rates.

Another example would be to say that the number of welding electrodes required to make a weld is proportional to the length of the plates, width of gap (type of preparation) and thickness of the plates. When the quantities increase together, or decrease together, the proportion is called *direct proportion*.

Inverse proportion

If one quantity goes up while the other goes down, this is called inverse proportion. As an example let's imagine an automatic welding machine again. Suppose a weld distance of 12 metres has to be made:

At a welding speed of 12 metres per hour, the weld would take 60 minutes
At 24 metres per hour, it would take 30 minutes
At 6 metres per hour, it would take 120 minutes
At 8 metres per hour, it would take 90 minutes
Notice that with inverse proportion, if we double one quantity, it halves the other.

135

Averages

In arithmetic, the *mean* of a set of numbers is found by finding the sum of the numbers and then dividing by the number of figures in the set. This is often called the 'average'. For example, the average of 8, 9, 7, 17, 19, and 18 is found by adding the numbers together:

$$8 + 9 + 7 + 17 + 19 + 18 = 78$$

and dividing the sum of the numbers by the number of figures in the set, in this case 6:

$$\frac{78}{6} = 13$$

So the average is 13.

The average is not necessarily an exact number – it may include a decimal. For example what is the average of 24, 20, 18, 21 and 15?

$$24 + 20 + 18 + 21 + 15 = 98$$

$$\frac{98}{5} = 19.6$$

So the average is 19.6

Here are some examples to practise:
Find the average of the following sets of numbers.
Set (a) 9, 15, 7, 12, 8.   Set (b) 30, 41, 35, 36, 45, 48.
Set (c) (as an example to find out an average weekly wage, if the amount varies)
£84, £120, £130, £90, £165, £180, £170, £175 (over an 8 week period)
Set (d) (as an example to calculate the average amount of welding electrodes consumed per hour in a medium sized fabrication workshop)
100, 250, 120, 60, 300, 220, 50, 90 (over an 8 hour period)

Useful Formulae

Key: l = Length d = Diameter
      b = Breadth r = Radius
      h = Perpendicular height P = Perimeter
      s = Side C = Circumference
      sh = Slant height A = Area
      V = Volume π = $\frac{22}{7}$ or 3.142

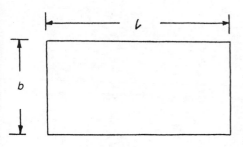

The Rectangle
$P = 2(l + b)$
$A = l \times b$

The Square
$P = 4s$
$A = s^2$

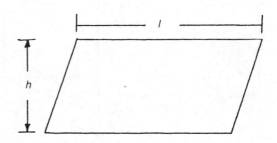

The Parallelogram
$P = 2(l + b)$
$A = l \times$ perpendicular height
(between measured length and one parallel to it)

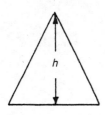

The Triangle
P = sum of three sides
$A = \frac{1}{2}$ (base $\times h$)

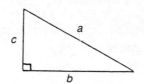

Right-Angled Triangle
$a^2 = b^2 + c^2$
$a = \sqrt{b^2 + c^2}$
$b = \sqrt{a^2 - c^2}$
$c = \sqrt{a^2 - b^2}$

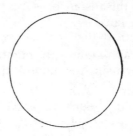

The Circle
$\pi = C \div d$
$C = \pi d$
$A = \pi r^2$

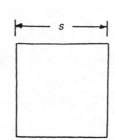

The Sphere
$A = 4\pi r^2$
$V = \frac{4}{3} \times \pi r^3$

Cylinder
Area of curved surface = $C \times h$
$V = \pi r^2 h$

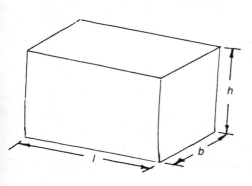

Volume of a Tank
$l \times b \times h$

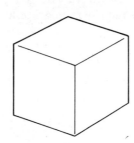

Solid
Area of 4 sides = $4s^2$
Total surface area
$A = 6s^2$

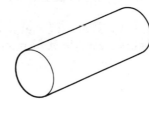

Cone
Area of curved surface
= $\frac{1}{2} C \times sh$
$V = \frac{1}{3} \pi r^2 h$

Welding Calculations for Practice

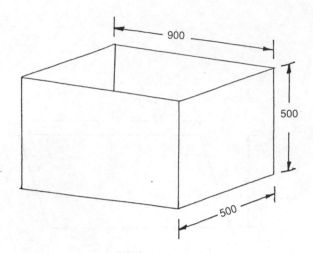

1. Fig Q1 shows an open top water tank to be fabricated from 5 pieces of 6 mm low carbon steel.
   (a) All welds are completed in one pass by the manual metal arc process. What will be the total length of weld per tank?
   (b) If welding is costed in this instance, as 75p per 100 mm, what will be the cost of welding one tank?

2. (a) Draw a straight-line graph to show the number of electrodes used by a company over one year, using the monthly figures given:

Jan.	Feb.	Mar.	Apr.	May	June
10,000	15,000	8,000	6,000	25,000	40,000

July	Aug.	Sept.	Oct.	Nov.	Dec.
60,000	50,000	20,000	10,000	9,000	7,000

   (b) What is the average amount of electrodes used per month?

3. A company uses electrodes 300 mm in length. If 50 mm is the average stub end loss, what percentage does this represent?

4. If a welding code requires 90% of welds on a fabrication to be radiographed and 120 welds are made, how many welds require radiographic testing?

5. What are the following % gas mixtures as fractions?
   (i) Argon – 25% CO_2 (ii) Argon – 2% O_2 (iii) Argon – 5% CO_2
   (iv) Argon – 2% O_2 – 5% CO_2.

Conductors, Resistors and Insulators

Materials that will be capable of carrying an electric current with a minimum of resistance are said to be good electrical conductors.

The thermal conductivity, that is, the ability to transfer heat by conduction through the material, is closely connected to its electrical conductivity. Copper, for example, is a better conductor of electricity than iron, although both materials will conduct electricity.

The fact that copper is also a better conductor of heat than iron can be proved by holding two rods, one of copper and one of iron or steel, and placing the ends of the rods in a flame. The copper rod will get hotter much faster than the steel one.

List of metals in order of thermal and electrical conductivity:
Silver
Copper
Aluminium
Zinc
Nickel
Iron
Steel
Tin
Lead

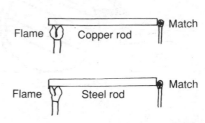

Copper rod will ignite match first, proving copper is a better conductor

Resistance

The electrical resistance of a conductor is based on the fact that all materials except superconductors will resist the flow of an electric current, converting a proportion of the electrical energy into heat. The extent to which a conductor will resist the flow of a given current will depend on its physical dimensions, the nature of the material from which it is made, its temperature and in some cases the extent to which it is illuminated, owing to photo-conductivity.

The element in an electric light bulb glows because of the heating effect caused by its resistance to flow, and an electric fire glows and gives off heat by resisting the flow of electricity.

Insulators

Insulators prevent the passage of electricity or heat. Not all insulators will do both – rubber and certain plastics are good insulators of electricity but will melt when exposed to higher levels of heat.

It is important to remember that there is no such thing as a perfect insulator, as all materials will allow the passage of electricity if a high enough pressure is applied.

In welding, where the voltages are generally low, glass, porcelain, rubber, mica and various plastics are used as insulators.

It must be mentioned that these insulators can fail if they become damp or wet, as water is a very good conductor of electricity. All electrical equipment should therefore be kept dry in order to avoid damage and the risk of electrocution.

Magnetism and Electricity

There is an ancient story about a Chinese general who, over 3,000 years ago, was pursuing his retreating foe when a thick fog descended, completely blotting out all landmarks. Any ordinary Chinese general may have well been forced to stop pursuit, but the ancient story says that this particular general had with him a chariot, in which stood an artificial figure, with outstretched arm that always pointed to the south. Directed by this weird and wonderful figure, the general soon caught up with his enemies and put them to rout.

This story is probably the first hint that the Chinese made use of 'magnetite' or black oxide of iron. It was well known by ancient peoples that a fragment of magnetite, when floated on a piece of wood, pointed one end to the Pole Star. To-day, we use the modern-day magnetic compass in the same way, the needle pointing to the Earth's magnetic north which is near to true north.

Commander James Ross discovered the magnetic north pole, and stated that when he arrived there all the compass needles appeared to have lost their power, as there was nowhere for them to point to. The same thing happened to Shackleton in 1909 when his expedition discovered the south magnetic pole.

Induction

Iron can be magnetised, and this process is called *induction*. When this happens, each small particle of the iron is supposed to become a tiny magnet with north and south poles. This in turn gives the bar of iron a north pole at one end and a south pole at the other, and if the bar were suspended on a piece of string, the north pole of the bar would of course point north.

Around every magnet there are invisible lines of magnetic force. These can be seen by placing a sheet of clear paper over the magnet and sprinkling iron filings on to the paper (see sketches).

When magnets are placed together, like poles will always repel each other and unlike poles will attract each other. These principles and the invisible but powerful lines of magnetic force given off from a magnet are used in the production of electricity.

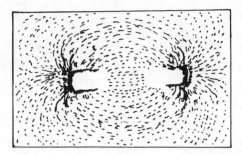

Magnetic field of a bar shown by placing paper over magnet and sprinkling iron filings over it

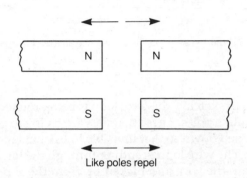

Like poles repel

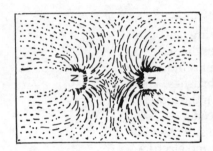

Repulsion between like poles

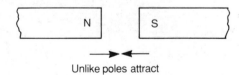

Unlike poles attract

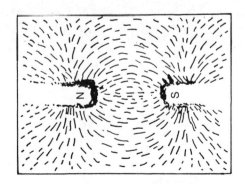

Attraction between unlike poles

Production of an Alternating Current

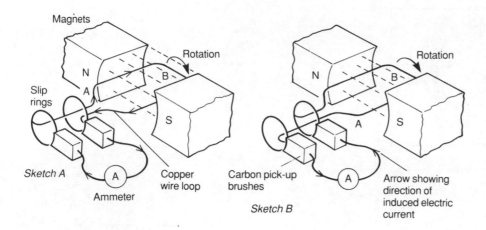

Three items are required to produce an electric current:
1. A magnetic field
2. A loop of copper wire
3. Movement of either the field or loop

In sketch A the wire loop is being rotated between two magnets with unlike poles. These magnets are trying to pull together, but they are fastened down so that invisible lines of magnetic force exist between them.

The wire loop is cutting through the lines of force and a current is induced into the wire and picked up from the slip rings by the carbon brushes. The current flow will be in the direction shown by the arrows. When the loop is vertical, no lines of force will be cut, so no current will be produced.

In sketch B, the wire loop has turned half a rotation and the side A–B is now on the right. The loop is again cutting through lines of force and electricity is induced into the loop in the same direction but, because of the position of the slip rings, it is picked up by the carbon brushes for use in the opposite direction – hence **alternating current** (AC) is being produced.

Production of Direct Current

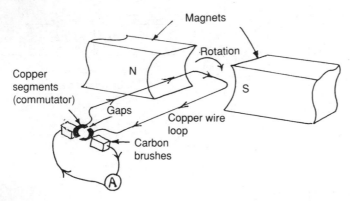

Both the production of AC and DC are similar, the only difference being in the method of pick up of the electricity.

AC generators use the two 'slip rings'. DC generators use the copper segments (commutators). Obviously, if the number of wire loops are increased and if four or more magnets are used, then the electrical power generated will be greater. This fact is used on industrial generators, but basically the design is the same as that shown above.

Electricity

There are two main sources of electrical power to consider from an engineering point of view. These are batteries and accumulators that generate electrical energy by chemical action, and generators that produce electrical energy by mechanical means.

For welding, generators of a special design are necessary. For welding with an alternating current, a transformer is used in order to change (or transform) the supply pressure to one suitable for welding.

A Simple Circuit

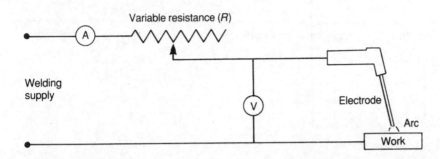

The figure above shows a circuit made up of an ammeter (A), a variable resistance (R), electrode holder, electrode and work. A voltmeter (V) is connected across the circuit.

When the electrode is touched to the work, the circuit is completed and the current will depend on the amount of resistance in the circuit.

If the electrode is lifted slightly from the work, say 4 mm, the current will still flow across the air gap between the end of the electrode and the work, in the form of an electric arc.

The amount of current flowing across the arc can be controlled by varying the amount of resistance (R) in the circuit. If a voltmeter (V) is placed across the circuit, it will register the drop in pressure which occurs as a result of the current being forced across the air gap between the electrode and the work. It will follow that the greater the gap between the electrode and the work, the greater will be the voltage drop, until the arc finally extinguishes itself when the gap becomes too great.

Electrical Resistance

All substances will offer some resistance to the passage of electricity, but some substances offer more resistance than others.

Good conductors such as copper and aluminium offer only small resistance but when in the form of wire or cable, their resistance will increase with length and decrease with cross-sectional area.

This is an important fact to remember when electric welding, because we need to try and keep voltage drop in the cable down to a minimum. Lengths of cable should therefore not be too long as there are obvious limits to increasing the cross-sectional area of cable.

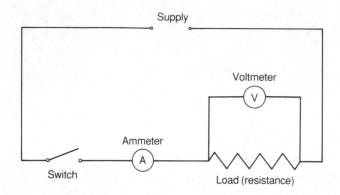

In the simple circuit shown above, we have a fixed electro-motive force (e.m.f.) which is the pressure available at the terminals of the generator when no current is flowing. This is known as the open-circuit voltage in welding.

The standard symbols for voltage current and resistance are:

Voltage = V
Current = I
Resistance = R

For welding purposes, we would use the ampere for the unit of current, the volt for the unit of e.m.f. or potential difference (drop across a circuit) and the ohm for the unit of resistance.

Ohm's Law

Ohms Law states that for any circuit, the current is proportional to the e.m.f. and inversely proportional to the resistance. This gives the useful formula:

$$I = \frac{V}{R}$$

It also gives:

$$\frac{V}{I} = R \quad \text{and} \quad V = I \times R$$

One way of remembering these formulae is to write down the letters in a triangle:

Then, by covering the unit required, its value in terms of the other units will be given. For example, if we cover V, it shows $I \times R$. If we cover R it shows $\frac{V}{I}$

Resistances Connected in Series and Parallel

In practical circuits, the various components can be connected together in different ways to produce different results.

No matter how complicated a circuit may be, it will be found to consist of two fundamental methods of connection, these being in series or in parallel.

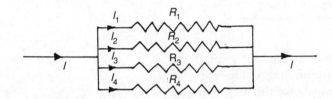

(Total resistance $R = R_1 + R_2 + R_3 + R_4$)

When resistances are connected in series, they are connected end to end, as shown in the sketch above. This gives only one path for the current. In such a case, the total resistance will be the sum of the individual resistances.

Resistances are said to be in parallel when they form separate branches of a circuit and when the total current fed to them is divided between them:

With parallel resistances, the reciprocal of the total resistance is the sum of the reciprocals of the branch resistances. Or, to use the example from the sketch above:

$$\frac{1}{R} = \frac{1}{R_1} + \frac{1}{R_2} + \frac{1}{R_3} + \frac{1}{R_4}$$

The Ammeter

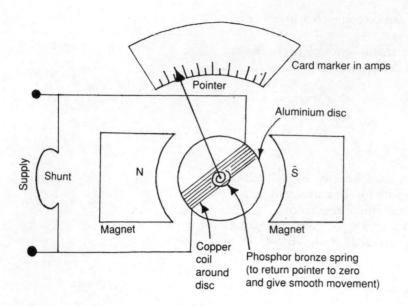

A large shunt (very good conductor) takes most of the current, but a small amount is fed through the coil wrapped round the aluminium disc. This current sets up a small magnetic field which tends to unbalance the magnetic force already in existence between the poles of the permanent magnets, and this unbalancing causes a turning action of the aluminium disc, which in turn moves the pointer.

The Voltmeter

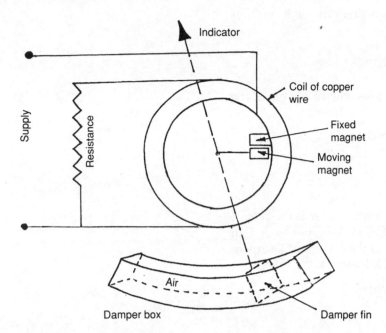

The volumeter is constructed so that a large resistance (say 100,000 ohms) takes most of the current. This means that the meter requires only a small coil to carry the remaining voltage and current.

$$\text{(By Ohm's Law, } I = \frac{V}{R} \text{; therefore } I = \frac{200 \text{ volts}}{100,000 \text{ ohms}} = 0.002 \text{ amp.)}$$

The coil induces magnetic fields into the two pieces of iron, making them magnets. Having like poles, these of course repel. The moving magnet turns the indicator needle, giving an indication of the voltage against a marked card placed behind the indicator point. The larger the voltage, the larger the magnetic field and therefore the greater the needle deflection.

Some arrangement must be fitted to prevent violent movement of the needle as the magnets act against each other. Several methods of slowing down the movement are used, including a phosphor bronze spring or a 'damper box' arrangement, such as the one shown in the sketch. The fin displacing the air in the box slows down the movement of the indicator.

Examples Using Ohm's in Simple Calculations

To find the resistance of a wire in ohms, when a pressure of 30 volts is applied with a current of 5 amps flowing:

$$R = \frac{V}{I} = \frac{30}{5} = 6 \text{ ohms resistance}$$

To find the voltage drop due to a resistance of 0.2 ohms when a current of 160 amps is flowing through it:

$$V = I \times R = 160 \times 0.2 = 32 \text{ volts drop}$$

The Watt

The amount of power in a circuit is given by the watt. Power is the rate of doing work and the watt is based on the amount of work done, per second, in a circuit where the difference of pressure is 1 volt, and a current of 1 ampere is flowing. This is classed as 1 watt. 1,000 watts = 1 kilowatt (kW). Therefore:

$$\text{Power in watts} = \text{volts} \times \text{amps.}$$

The Joule

The joule is the unit of work, energy and quantity of heat (J). A joule is the amount of work done when a force of 1 newton (N) moves a distance of 1 metre (m). 1 watt (W) = 1 joule per second (J/s). The newton is defined as a force which, when acting on a mass of 1 kilogram (kg), will give it an acceleration of 1 metre per second per second (1 m/s^2).

As an example, to find the output of a welding generator in kilowatts and joules per second, if the output is 90 volts, 200 amps:

$$90 \times 200 = 18,000 \text{ W} = 18 \text{ kW} \ \& \ 18,000 \text{ J/s}$$

This calculation gives the output of the generator. The power required to drive a generator will always be greater because of frictional and other losses. As a rough estimate of power required to drive a welding generator in kW, it is usual to add on half the output. In the case of the generator given here, this would be 18 + 9 = 27 kW.

The unit on which electricity companies base the charge for customers is the kilowatt hour (kWh); this is usually classed as 1 unit of electricity.

APPENDIX A: GENERAL WELDING AND CUTTING TERMS

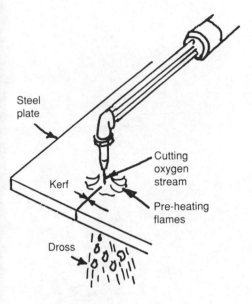

Oxy/fuel gas cutting

Kerf: The width of cut

Toe of weld: Where the weld face joins the parent metal.

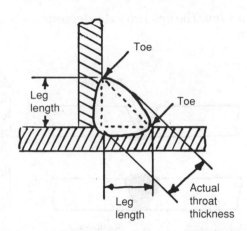

Gap: The distance between the parts to be joined.

Heat affected zone: The parts of the parent metal where the structure has been changed by the heat of welding but not melted.

Included angle: The angle between the fusion faces.

Parent metal: The material(s) to be welded.

Leg length: The size of a fillet weld is given by the leg length (see sketch)

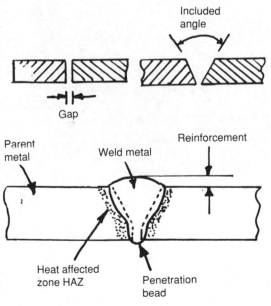

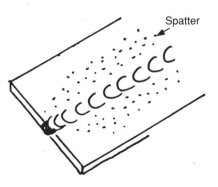

Throat thickness: The shortest distance from the root of a fillet weld to the weld face. In a butt weld, it is the thickness of weld melt measured at the centre line.

Spatter: Globules of metal thrown out from the arc area during welding.

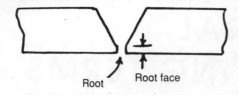

Root: The point at the base of a prepared joint where the material to be joined is closest together. In a square butt joint, the root will be the fusion faces furthest from the weld faces.

Root

Root face

Root face: The squared root edges designed to aid penetration.

Root run: The first run to be deposited in a joint requiring more than one weld run.

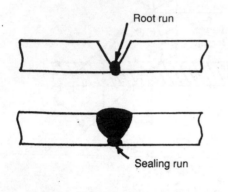

Root run

Sealing run

Backing bar: A piece of metal or other material placed under a weld to aid good penetration formation but not intended to become part of the welded joint.

Backing strip: A piece of metal positioned at the root of the joint and becoming part of the welded joint.

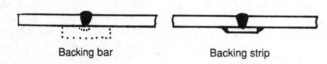

Backing bar   Backing strip

Sealing run: A small weld deposited on the root side of a butt or corner joint, after the main weld has been completed.

APPENDIX B: SPECIMEN QUESTIONS FOR THE 165 CERTIFICATE IN WELDING PRACTICE LEVEL 1

THE WELDING INSTITUTE
EAST MIDLAND FURTHER EDUCATION COUNCIL
NORTH WESTERN REGIONAL ASSOCIATION OF
EDUCATION AUTHORITIES (CENTRA).

165–1 CERTIFICATE IN WELDING PRACTICE (LEVEL 1)

SPECIMEN QUESTIONS

165–1–01 UNIT 1 GAS WELDING AND CUTTING
154–1–02 UNIT 2 MANUAL METAL ARC WELDING
165–1–03 UNIT 3 METAL ARC GAS-SHIELDED WELDING
165–1–04 UNIT 4 TUNGSTEN ARC GAS-SHIELDED WELDING
165–1–06 UNIT 6 RELATED STUDIES

Each of the above papers will contain two sections to be answered in 1 hour.

Section A (10 marks) will contain ten multiple choice questions carrying 1 mark each.

Section B (20 marks) will contain ten short answer questions carrying 2 marks each.

The following specimen questions and answers are provided to illustrate the type of question which will be set and the depth of treatment of the syllabus. Two or three of each type of question are given for each paper.

SECTION A

Section A has ten multiple choice questions carrying 1 mark each.
UNIT 1 GAS WELDING AND CUTTING

A1. One effect of too low a gas velocity when oxy-actylene welding is
   (A) too much heat
   (B) oxidation of the weld pool
   (C) reduction of the weld pool
   (D) backfiring at the blowpipe

                                                             D

A2. The correct pre-heat flame setting for oxy-acetylene cutting low carbon
steel is
(A) neutral
(B) oxidising
(C) carburising
(D) slightly oxidising

A

UNIT 2 MANUAL METAL ARC WELDING

A3. The welding arc voltage will be raised if there is an increase in the
(A) pre-heat temperature
(B) arc conductivity
(C) arc length
(D) open-circuit voltage

C

A4. The weld defect indicated by arrow A in the figure below is called
(A) overlap
(B) under cut
(C) lack of root penetration
(D) insufficient reinforcement

C

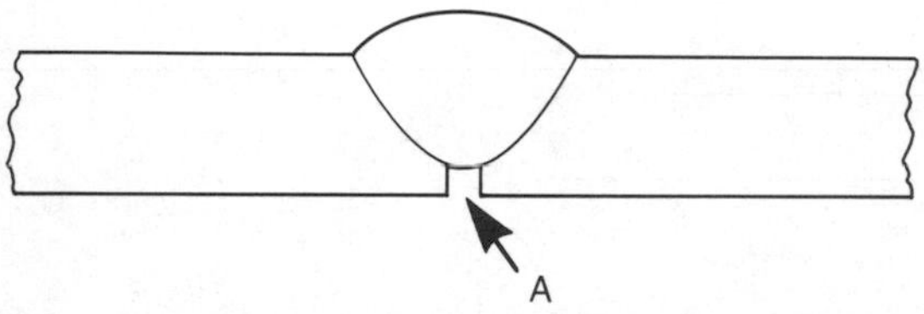

UNIT 3 METAL ARC GAS-SHIELDED WELDING

A5. When using the gas-shielded metal arc process for the welding of low
carbon steel, a suitable shielding gas mixture would be
(A) nitrogen and oxygen
(B) hydrogen and oxygen
(C) argon and nitrogen
(D) argon and carbon dioxide

D

A6. Visual examination of a multi-run single vee butt weld would NOT
reveal
(A) undercut
(B) weld contour
(C) slag inclusions
(D) lack of penetration

C

UNIT 4 TUNGSTEN ARC GAS-SHIELDED WELDING

A7. The recommended method of initiating a tungsten arc gas-shielded
welding arc is by
(A) a suppressor
(B) a high-frequency unit
(C) contacting the workpiece
(D) an economizer

B

A8. When tungsten arc gas-shielded welding, the arc length is controlled by the
(A) shape of electrode tip
(B) contactor unit
(C) high-frequency unit
(D) skill of the operator

| D |

UNIT 6 RELATED STUDIES

A9. The unit of electrical resistance is called the
(A) ohm
(B) volt
(C) watt
(D) ampere

| A |

A10. The flame temperature of a neutral oxy-acetylene flame is approximately
(A) 2,400°C
(B) 2,600°C
(C) 2,800°C
(D) 3,200°C

| D |

A11. In a welding circuit, the voltage is 240 volts and the current 12 amperes. What is the resistance of the circuit?
(A) 20 ohms
(B) 24 ohms
(C) 48 ohms
(D) 2,280 ohms

| A |

SECTION B

Section B has ten short answer questions carrying 2 marks each.
UNIT 1 GAS WELDING AND CUTTING

B1. State TWO methods of identifying gas cylinders according to BS349.

(a) *colour* ....

(b) *thread* ....

1 mark each

B2. State TWO methods of supplying oxygen for welding or cutting purposes.

(a) *cylinders* ....

(b) *liquid bulk supplies* ....

1 mark each

B3. Name TWO types of oxy-acetylene flames.

(a) *neutral, carburising, oxidising* ....

(b) ....

Any two 1 mark each

UNIT 2 MANUAL METAL ARC WELDING

B4. State TWO essential characteristics of a welding lead cable.

(a) *current capacity, insulated, flexible* ....

(b) ....

Any two 1 mark each

B5. Name the TWO electrode polarities associated with a DC welding arc.

(a) *positive* ....

(b) *negative* ....

1 mark each

UNIT 3 METAL ARC GAS-SHIELDED WELDING

B6. State the function of a flowmeter.

Visual indication of gas flow rate ....

....

2 marks

B7. State how welding current affects burn-off rate.

Increased welding current increases burn-off rate and vice versa ....

. ...

2 marks

B8. Name TWO possible defects which may occur during metal arc gas-shielded welding.

(a) *undercut, porosity, lack of fusion, lack of penetration,* ....

(b) *cracking* ....

Any two 1 mark each

UNIT 4 TUNGSTEN ARC GAS-SHIELDED WELDING

B9. State the purpose of a high-frequency unit used in conjunction with the tungsten arc gas-shielded welding process.

Arc initiation ....

To enable AC welding to take place ....

Any one 2 marks

B10. Name TWO inert gases which may be used when tungsten arc gas-shielded welding.

(a) *Argon* ....

(b) *Helium* ....

1 mark each

B11. State why tungsten arc gas-shielded welding should NOT be used in windy conditions.

Wind may blow away shielding gas ....

....

2 marks

UNIT 5 FABRICATION PROCESSES

B12. With the aid of a simple sketch, show how the joint gap for a butt joint in sheet steel may be pre-set to reduce distortion.

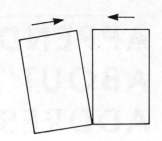

2 marks

UNIT 6 RELATED STUDIES

B13. (a) Name ONE gas which is an element.

  e.g. oxygen, hydrogen, argon ....

1 mark

(b) Name ONE gas which is a compound.

  e.g. acetylene, propane, butane, carbon dioxide ....

1 mark

B14. State TWO functions of a flux as used in manual metal arc welding.

  (a) *To clean the weld area, to provide gaseous shield protection,* ....

  (b) *to slow the cooling rate, etc.* ....

Any two 1 mark each

B15. Define the term toughness related to material properties.

  The property which enables a material to resist impact ....

2 marks

APPENDIX C: INFORMATION ABOUT TWI AND SOME USEFUL ADDRESSES

TWI

TWI, world centre for materials joining technology, is unique. It is a large research and development establishment as well as a professional engineering institution and learned society, committed to the transfer of information to industry.

It is the largest contract research organisation in materials engineering and joining technology in the Western world, with a multi-million pound investment in specialised equipment and facilities. With a staff of over 400 it supports some 2,500 companies throughout the world. It works in partnership with the Edison Welding Institute in the USA, each organisation having access to all of the other's facilities.

As a research contractor, TWI undertakes work in confidence for both industry and governments. As a consultant, it can field individual experts or teams able to deal with both simple and complex problems of design, materials selection, production, economics and quality control. It will send specialist staff anywhere in the world at short notice on trouble-shooting missions.

TWI's business is the totality of joining of engineering materials – metals or non-metals – by the most appropriate process or technique, such as welding, adhesive bonding, brazing etc. Its principal areas of technical activity are:

Engineering: design and structural integrity of engineering fabrications, that is, the assessment of strength, toughness and life of components.

Materials: understanding and quantifying effects of welding on properties and structure of materials.

Non-destructive Testing (NDT): determining the quality or soundness of welded or bonded materials and developing testing techniques.

Lasers: use of high power lasers in welding, cutting, drilling and surface treatment.

Electron Beam: designing beam generation, control and power supply equipment, and applications studies.

Arc Welding: research and contract work on conventional welding, surfacing and cutting processes.

Forge and Resistance Processes: developing and applying conventional and advanced resistance, friction and other forge process technology, prototype component and equipment manufacture, subcontracting.

Manufacturing Systems: computer integrated manufacture, advanced manufacturing systems, factory automation and robotics.

Plastics Joining: improving quality and reliability of plastics joining processes.

Ceramics and Precision Processes: joining techniques for ceramics and micro-electronics, and diffusion bonding and brazing process development.

TWI is also a communicator of technical information, and an organiser of conferences, seminars and group meetings of specialists. It is a training centre for all aspects of welding and non-destructive testing, a centre for welding information from world sources with the latest data processing techniques and a provider of data and software for computers.

As 'The Welding Institute', it is a professional institution which has established standards of qualification for its individual, corporate and technician members. As a learned society, it provides opportunities for the exchange of information among its members and it maintains contact with welding organisations overseas, being a leading supporter of the International Institute of Welding.

In summary, the aims of TWI are to:

- Help improve manufacturing efficiency;
- Promote safe use of welding and joining in fabricated structures and components;
- Encourage innovation of new products through better design, materials selection and manufacturing methods.

Useful Addresses

TWI
The Welding Institute
Abington Hall
Abington
Cambridge CB1 6AL

World Centre for materials joining technology

CENTRA
Town Hall
Walkden Road
Worsley
Manchester M28 4QE

Information on welding courses

EMFEC
Robins Wood House
Robins Wood Road
Aspley
Nottingham NG8 3NH

Information on welding courses

BSI
Enquiry Service
Linford Wood
Milton Keynes, MK14 6LE

British Standards relating to welding

City and Guilds of London Institute
76 Portland Place
London W1N 4AA

Information on welding courses

American Welding Society
550 N.W. Lejeune Road
PO Box 351040
Miami
Florida 33135
USA

Main welding centre in the USA. General welding information, details of membership, books, magazines etc.

The James F. Lincoln Arc
Welding Foundation
Mansfield Road
Aston
Sheffield S31 0BS

Welding books. A charitable educational foundation devoted entirely to welding education

The British Oxygen Company Ltd
The Priestley Centre
10 Priestley Road
The Surrey Research Park
Guildford
Surrey GU2 5XY

Information on welding products

British Federal Ltd
Castle Mill Works
Birmingham New Road
Dudley
West Midlands DY1 4DA

Information on resistance welding

WESCOL Ltd
Welding Products
PO BOX 41
Wolverhampton WV1 3EA

Information on welding products

Frost Auto Restoration Techniques Ltd
Crawford Street
Rochdale OL16 5NU

Specialist tools and equipment for
auto restoration and fabrication

Co-Weld
197 Caryl Street
Liverpool, L8 6UU

Suppliers of welding equipment,
manipulators and positioners

Murex Welding Products Ltd
Hertford Road
Waltham Cross
Herts EN8 7RP

Gas and electric welding
equipment

Thomas A. Metcalfe Ltd
Market Street
Droylsden
Manchester M35 7DJ

Suppliers of welding equipment

AWTE
Association for Welding Training and Education
c/o: TWI

Some Other Useful Addresses of Commercial Firms

AGA Ltd
New Cut Industrial Estate
Woolston
Warrington
Cheshire WA1 4AG
Tel: 0925 811543
Fax: 0925 821735
Telex: 627315

Arcos Lincoln Electric Ltd
Hertford Road
Waltham Cross
Herts EN8 7RP
Tel: 0992 701118
Fax: 0992 719191
Telex: 25743

BIG Central Distribution
New Cut Industrial Estate
Woolston
Warrington
Cheshire WA1 4AG
Tel: 0925 811005
Fax: 0925 821735
Telex: 627315

Brinal Ltd
Hertford Road
Waltham Cross
Herts EN8 7RP
Tel: 0992 768711
Fax: 0992 719191
Telex: 25743

ESAB Ltd
Hertford Road
Waltham Cross
Herts EN8 7RP
Tel: 0992 760698
Fax: 0992 719191
Telex: 25743

Murex Gas Control Equipment
Hertford Road
Waltham Cross
Herts EN8 7RP
Tel: 0992 714777
Fax: 0992 719191
Telex: 25743

ESAB Automation Ltd
Crown Way
Walworth Industrial Estate
Andover
Hants SP10 5LU
Tel: 0264 332233
Fax: 0264 332074
Telex: 47458

Filarc Welding Products Ltd
Hertford Road
Waltham Cross
Herts EN8 7RP
Tel: 0992 88511
Fax: 0992 719191
Telex: 25743

ESAB Group (UK) Ltd
Training Centre
Plume Street
Aston
Birmingham B6 7RU
Tel: 021 328 2711
Fax: 021 327 4341

L-Tec Welding and Cutting Systems
Ellesmere House
Holyoake Road
Worsley
Manchester M28 5DF
Tel: 061 703 8539
Fax: 061 703 8512

Murex Welding Products Ltd
Hertford Road
Waltham Cross
Herts EN8 7RP
Tel: 0992 710000
Fax: 0992 719191
Telex: 25743

APPENDIX D: METRIC AND IMPERIAL MEASURES

Metric Measures

Length

1 millimetre (mm)		= 0.0394 in.
1 centimetre (cm)	= 10 mm	= 0.3937 in.
1 metre (m)	= 100 cm	= 1.0936 yd
1 kilometre (km)	= 1,000 m	= 0.6214 mile

Area

1 sq cm (cm^2)	= 100 mm^2	= 0.1550 in.^{2}
1 sq metre (m^2)	= 10,000 cm^2	= 1.1960 yd^2
1 sq km (km^2)	= 100 hectares	= 0.3861 mile^2

Volume/Capacity

1 cu cm (cm^3)		= 0.0610 in^3
1 cu decimetre (dm^3)	= 1,000 cm^3	= 0.0353 ft^3
1 cu metre (m^3)	= 1,000 dm^3	= 1.3080 yd^3
1 litre (l)	= 1 dm^3	= 1.76 pt
		= 2.113 US liq pt
1 hectolitre (hl)	= 100 l	= 21.998 gal
		= 26.418 US gal

Mass (Weight)

1 milligram (mg)		= 0.0154 grain
1 gram (g)	= 1,000 mg	= 0.0353 oz
1 metric carat	= 0.2 g	= 3.0865 grains
1 kilogram (kg)	= 1,000 g	= 2.2046 lb
1 tonne (t)	= 1,000 kg	= 0.9842 ton
		= 1.1023 short ton

Temperature Conversion

$$C = \frac{5}{9}(F - 32) \quad F = \frac{9}{5}C + 32$$

Imperial and US Measures

Length

1 inch (in.)		= 2.54 cm
1 foot (ft)	= 12 in.	= 0.3048 m
1 yard (yd)	= 3 ft	= 0.9144 m
1 mile	= 1,760 yd	= 1.6093 km
1 int nautical mile	= 2,025.4 yd	= 1.852 km

Area

1 sq inch (in.^{2})		= 6.4516 cm^2
1 sq foot (ft^2)	= 144 in.^{2}	= 0.0929 m^2
1 sq yard (yd^2)	= 9 ft^2	= 0.8361 m^2
1 acre	= 4,840 yd^2	= 4046.9 m^2
1 sq mile (mile^2)	= 640 acres	= 2.590 km^2

Volume/Capacity

1 cu inch (in^3)		= 16.387 cm^3
1 cu foot (ft^3)	= 1,728 in^3	= 0.0283 m^3
1 cu yard (yd^3)	= 27 ft^3	= 0.7646 m^3
1 liquid ounce (fl oz)		= 28.413 ml
1 pint (pt)	= 20 fl oz	= 0.5683 l
1 gallon (gal)	= 8 pt	= 4.546 l

Mass (Weight)

1 ounce (oz)	= 437.5 grains	= 28.35 g
1 pound (lb)	= 16 oz	= 0.4536 kg
1 stone	= 14 lb	= 6.3503 kg
1 hundredweight (cwt)	= 112 lb	= 50.802 kg
1 ton	= 20 cwt	= 1.016 t

US Measures

1 US dry pint	= 33.60 in^3	= 0.5506 l
1 US liquid pint	= 0.8327 imp pt	= 0.4732 l
1 US gallon	= 0.8327 imp gal	= 3.785 l
1 short cwt	= 100 lb	= 45.359 kg
1 short ton	= 2,000 lb	= 907.10 kg

INDEX